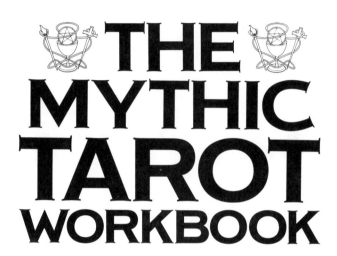

THE MYTHIC TAROT WORKBOOK

JULIET SHARMAN·BURKE

COAUTHOR OF *THE MYTHIC TAROT*

A Fireside Book
Published by Simon & Schuster
New York London Toronto Sydney Singapore

To Jessica with love

FIRESIDE
Rockefeller Center
1230 Avenue of the Americas
New York, NY 10020

Text copyright © 1988 by Juliet Sharman-Burke
Card illustrations copyright © 1986 by Tricia Newell
This edition copyright © 1988 by Eddison/Sadd Editions Limited

This Fireside Edition 2001

FIRESIDE and colophon are registered trademarks of
Simon & Schuster Inc.

For information regarding special discounts for bulk purchases,
please contact Simon & Schuster Special Sales:
1-800-456-6798 or business@simonandschuster.com

Designed by Amanda Barlow

Manufactured in the United States of America

10 9 8 7 6 5 4 3 2 1

Library of Congress Cataloging-in-Publication Data is available.

ISBN 0-7432-2307-1

AN EDDISON · SADD EDITION
Edited, designed and produced by
Eddison/Sadd Editions Limited
St Chad's Court, 146B Kings Cross Road,
London WC1X 9DH

Phototypeset by Bookworm Typesetting, Manchester, England
Origination by Columbia Offset, Singapore
Printing, binding and manufacture in the United States of America

CONTENTS

INTRODUCTION

This Workbook is intended to help Tarot students to deepen and widen their knowledge of the cards. I have had the good fortune to teach many Beginners' Workshops in Tarot which often ended with the cry: 'Now that we know what the cards *mean* how do we *work* with them?' In answer to that cry I set up Advanced Workshops. This Workbook is intended to act as a substitute for workshops. It is a sequel to *The Mythic Tarot*, which provided background history for all forms of Tarot cards, and outlined the basic meanings in a mythological, psychological and divinatory sense.

Although the Workbook is designed with *The Mythic Tarot* cards in mind, it can be used equally well with any other Tarot deck with which readers may be more familiar. The mythic pictorial imagery differs from many traditional Tarot decks but the divinatory meanings of the cards remain the same. The exercises are therefore appropriate for use with any Tarot deck. The Workbook aims to help students to structure and increase their knowledge in using the Tarot more effectively in practice. So it concentrates on the two aspects essential to all effective Tarot readings: that readers come to know themselves better via the Tarot, and that they in turn use their knowledge to help interpreting it for other people.

The Workbook comprises four parts. The first deals with the Major Arcana and concentrates on developing a richer and deeper relationship with the mysterious twenty-two Major Trumps. Guided fantasy and therapeutic colouring exercises are demonstrated in order to enable you to establish a closer relationship with the images. Particular attention is paid to the cards' uses and their value in the search for self-awareness. The second section focuses on the Court Cards and their correlation with Astrology, in particular with zodiacal sun signs through the Knight, Queen and King. The third section offers a closer understanding of the everyday meanings of the Minor Arcana, and space is provided for exercises to help fix their message clearly in the reader's understanding. The fourth section looks at various aspects of Tarot reading, layouts and use of the Tarot therapeutically; whether professionally, for friends, or for personal self-improvement.

It is important to remember that your proficiency in Tarot readings will be directly linked with the amount of effort put into study. For this reason I have devised various exercises to help you to develop a greater understanding of interpretation. Methodical performance of these exercises will produce a deeper appreciation of the breadth and depth of this fascinating subject. The exercises are structured and set out in a form that encourages you to fill in the blanks and note pages. Keeping a conscientious record of your work over weeks, months and years will develop a continuity in study, as well as charting your progress. In attempting the colouring exercises it is a good idea to record the date and your mood at the time, so that in weeks or months ahead you can look back over your notes and see how your views have changed and developed. Similarly, keeping a record of the readings you perform on the blanks provided, will act as a reminder of the outcome of your own interpretations and those made for friends or clients. I recommend that you open a file to contain photocopies of the blank spreads to facilitate this.

The style and manner of your approach to reading Tarot will naturally be unique to you. Within the generally accepted principles and symbolism of Tarot, a spread of cards is capable of interpretation in many ways, depending upon one's personal experience. I can offer an insight into my own approach to interpretation, but it will not necessarily be the same as your own. Tarot reading is a deeply personal act which can only develop with time and effort and practice.

EXERCISES FOR THE MAJOR ARCANA

Therapeutic Colouring

The layout of the first twenty-two pages of the Workbook shows The Mythic Tarot card on the left hand page and an enlarged black-and-white outline on the opposite page. Colouring these black-and-white images can help to stimulate and increase latent powers of intuition. Fantasy and imagination are the means for stimulating the intuitive powers which are present in all of us but which lie deep in the unconscious mind. An effective way of unleashing this dormant creative potential is to release the 'child' part of ourselves and let the imagination flow. Children are not shackled by inhibitions and can let their feelings flow unchecked. Their painting, drawing and colouring games help to develop their imagination, broaden their horizons, air their emotions and resolve inner conflict. As adults we become conscious of our inadequacy in artistic achievement, and so shy away from attempting to represent our emotions pictorially. Yet painting and colouring have great potential for expressing thoughts and concentrating energy.

Colouring the outlined images of The Mythic Tarot Major Arcana enables you to surrender to the image's symbolism and message and establish a rapport with its deeper meaning. So, allow yourself to suspend intellectual judgement for a short while and let your imagination roam freely around a particular image; and then see how effortlessly feelings and associations can emerge spontaneously. Let your choices in colour flow, too, because this exercise is not artistic but therapeutic. Make a free choice of the colours which seem to you most appropriate in describing the essence of each card. Think about feelings the different colours evoke in you: does green symbolise for you a sinister feeling of envy or a calm assurance of the natural order of things? Does red signify anger or energy? Does yellow imply cowardice or splendour? Colours in The Mythic Tarot Minor Arcana cards attempt to reflect the mood of the image in general terms – blues for the watery suit of Cups, reds and oranges for the fiery Wands, silvers and greys for the airy Swords and browns and greens for the earthy Pentacles.

These may not coincide with your own impressions: you should feel free to choose the colours which best express your personal inclination. Try to find a key colour to associate with each Major card.

In working through this exercise, record the date in each case and make brief notes of your thoughts, feelings and memories at the time. On returning to one or the other of the images on later occasions the chosen colours may stimulate different, possibly more vivid associations.

As an example, consider the image of the Empress. In The Mythic Tarot she is represented as the Earth Mother, the goddess Demeter, and is therefore closely associated with the Mother-image, personal and archetypal. In setting out to discover more about this card, start by colouring her image. Like Demeter, mothers have two aspects: one dark and the other light. One set of colours might be adopted for exploring her dark face and another set for her bright face. This exercise affords a valuable opportunity to explore the various Mother-associations: your own mother, the mother within you, yourself as a mother, and so on.

The journey through the Major Arcana is an archetypal one. Each of the Major Trumps depicts a stage of human development. The Greeks identified the many and various human emotions and projected them onto their gods and goddesses, thus bringing the emotion to life. As you study each of the twenty-two Major Arcana, employing the techniques of therapeutic colouring and guided fantasy, you will start to recognise the various gods and goddesses within your own psyche, and the image which each portrays. Dwelling on the myth pertaining to each card will help you fit the myth into that uniquely fascinating story of which you are the author, namely your life.

It is important to identify our individual experience of each of the archetypal situations which touch our lives. Everyone can recognise an element of individual experience associated with the Empress, for example, of motherhood. But each person's experience will be different. By using the Tarot to deepen our understanding of ourselves, we can in turn broaden our understanding of others. This is an essential stage if we are to use the Tarot therapeutically.

Guided Fantasy Exercises

It is useful to complete your colouring exercise first and then let the image develop within. For this exercise, it is important to select a quiet time during which you feel confident of remaining uninterrupted. Choose a comfortable chair or lie down. Now breathe deeply. Breathe in counting slowly to four. Hold your breath to the count of four. Now breathe out to the count of four. Relax for a moment and repeat the exercise twice. Let every muscle in your body tense up and then relax. When you feel fully relaxed, let yourself drift into a truly peaceful state.

Now call to mind the image you have been working on in your colouring exercise. If, for example, it was the Empress, construct her image in your mind and visualise the exact picture of the card. When you can recall the image vividly – and this may take a short while – imagine the scene as though it could be seen through a window frame. Imagine you are climbing through the frame and now find yourself standing in the Empress' bright landscape. Imagine you are standing in a field of corn and flowers. Take note of the countryside, the waterfall, the fruit and vegetation. Use the imagery given at the end of each Major Arcana card as a guide. Allow your imagination to take you wherever you would like to go, but always keep within the context of the card. Strike up a conversation with the Empress and talk for as long as you wish. When you feel ready to stop, imagine that you are climbing back out of the window frame into your own world again. Only when you can see the card once more as a flat, one-dimensional image may you open your eyes and return to everyday life. Now write down your impressions, feelings, associations, details of the conversation, the memories it evoked and so on. It may help to tape-record it. Although it may seem difficult at first, and might make you feel a little silly, do persevere because the results will be well worthwhile.

THE FOOL

Mythological reference: Dionysus
Divinatory meaning: *A new phase of life begins, a risk must be taken, a need to abandon the old and start something new.*

The Fool starts off the procession of the Major Arcana and his journey through the Trumps is not unlike the archetypal journey through life which we all make. The Fool, therefore, stands for each of us as we embark on a new stage in our lives. The god Dionysus, who personifies the Fool in *The Mythic Tarot*, was an ambivalent character. His dual parentage, mortal and divine, is reflected by the eagle of his heavenly father Zeus, and by the goat horns of earthly nature. We share in this same duality as we seek to find spiritual understanding and purpose while still partaking of earthly life, pain and pleasure.

When the Fool appears in a reading he often suggests that the time for change is nigh. The 'sane' rational voice within may suggest it would be wiser to stay put, but the spirit of change which the Fool embodies is often stronger. For example, I once did a reading for a woman who had the Fool in the centre of her spread. She told me she was in the process of selling the house she had lived in for well over forty years, which had been her mother's home too. There was nothing particularly wrong with the house and her friends all told her she was mad to uproot herself. But she told me that she simply could not help herself. Amidst all her uncertainties and doubts as to where her move might lead, she nevertheless felt a strong irreversible need to cast aside her old life and start something new. Psychologically, it implied cutting final ties with her mother. Thus the

THE FOOL

Fool is depicted leaving the safety of the maternal womblike cave. In order to stand alone, we need to have the courage to leave behind the safety of the nest.

As you colour the image dwell on the feelings evoked by the figure dancing gaily on the cliff's edge. Does it bring feelings of adventure and excitement, or fear and dread? Make sure you choose colours which echo your feelings. Can you find a key colour to associate with this card? Explore the relationship with the Fool in you. Is it an easy or uneasy one? When have you found yourself poised on the edge of change? Did you happily take the plunge or did you hold back and cling to the status quo? Does the Fool evoke memories of the risks of youth? He does, after all, reflect something of the child in us, and the carefree way he dances on the edge of potential danger is evocative of the lack of fear typically displayed by children. The innocent trust in life gradually turns to suspicion as we get older. To be in touch with the Fool is to be in touch with trust in life's goodness; and somehow those who truly trust seem to be well rewarded.

As you embark on your guided fantasy exercise imagine yourself to be standing in the landscape of the Fool. Feel the watery warmth of the early morning sun as you leave the cool darkness of the cave. See the barren desert-like valley below. Now turn to meet the Fool who stands beside you. Imagine the conversation and record your impressions.

Name:

Date:

Place:

Your key colour:

Notes and observations about your colouring/guided fantasy exercise:

THE MAGICIAN

Mythological reference: Hermes
Divinatory meaning: New skills and potentials available, opportunities and adventures unfolding.

The Magician corresponds to the god Hermes, who, in myth, was the half-brother of Dionysus, the Fool. Hermes was a tricky yet charming character, renowned for his mischievous pranks yet beloved by the gods for his help in all manner of delicate situations. He was the messenger who communicated between earth and the heavens, between gods and men. On an inner level he acts as a guide between the conscious daylight world and the dark hidden unconscious recesses of the psyche. He brings to light knowledge which is unknown to our conscious minds. He may appear as a flash of intuition which often defies logic and yet is unerringly accurate. We often find ourselves acting against our instincts and doing what is rationally acceptable, usually with unsatisfactory results. If we have the courage to listen to the dictates of the Magician within us, the benefits can be richly rewarding.

When we are in tune with the Magician within, life does not seem quite so perilous. The strange intuition of the Magician is reflected in Hermes' skill in divination. This skill awarded him mastery of the four elements: Water, Fire, Air and Earth, symbolised in the Minor Arcana suits as Cup, Wand, Sword and Pentacle. The Magician stands for the inner guide who firmly yet kindly prompts us to develop and fulfill our potential. He offers us opportunities in the area of feelings (the Cups), creative imagination (the Wands), intellect (the Swords)

THE MAGICIAN

and of the material world (the Pentacles). The four symbols laid out before him represent the tools he offers us to aid in exploring these four realms of experience.

As you prepare to colour in his image, try to capture in your colours his quick-silver mercurial qualities. Try in this way to contact the part in you that the Magician represents. Find a key colour which sums up his essence for you. As you concentrate on colouring in the Cup, Wand, Sword and Pentacle think about what meaning these objects have for you. Let yourself dwell upon the qualities and character of Hermes, the Magician. Is he a helpful figure? Can you trust your own intuitions or are you afraid to let yourself surrender to the irrational? Give some thought to the intuitive powers reflected by the Magician, the 'sixth sense', the part in you which 'knows' on a deep level that which your conscious mind can barely glimpse.

To start your guided fantasy exercise imagine yourself to be at a dusty crossroads. There are four paths to choose from and four objects laid out before the figure of the Magician. It is hot and the landscape is barren. The Magician adds a splash of colour to the scene in his scarlet cloak and pure white tunic. Which of the objects laid out would you most like to pick up? Which appeals the least? Start your conversation with the Magician, carefully recording it after you have completed the exercise in fantasy.

Name:

Date:

Place:

Your key colour:

Notes and observations about your colouring/guided fantasy exercise:

THE EMPRESS

Mythological reference: Demeter
Divinatory meaning: Fertility, creativity, abundance, marriage or relationship, children.

The Empress is depicted in *The Mythic Tarot* as the mother goddess of nature, Demeter. The myth of Demeter and her daughter Persephone illustrates clearly both the love and fulfilment, as well as the difficulties and limitations, which motherhood brings. When Persephone was abducted by Hades, the harsh unforgiving side of Demeter's nature was evoked and she refused to rest until she had her daughter by her side once again. Through clever manipulation and blackmail, Demeter obtained a compromise and Persephone was returned to live with her mother for nine months of every year. The myth does not reveal anything about Persephone's feelings regarding her mother's actions and demands. What it does reveal, however, is that Persephone deliberately put herself at risk by straying out of the safety of her mother's sight to pick flowers. We are also told that she voluntarily ate the seeds of the pomegranate, fruit of conjugal love, which suggests that her loss of innocence was not altogether undesired. Nonetheless she obeys her mother's wishes and returns for part of each year to Demeter's bright sunlit world, though no words are ever spoken about the dark months she spends with her underworld husband. Does she comply with Demeter just to please her powerful mother or can Persephone herself not cope with the separation? How many of us cannot follow our true wishes and desires because they conflict with those of our mothers? And how

THE EMPRESS

many mothers can genuinely allow their children to make mistakes, get hurt, 'make a mess of their lives'? The first, and therefore most significant relationship we form, is with our mother and this first relationship has a bearing on all the relationships we form subsequently. Although our experience may not be as dramatic as choosing between the earth and the underworld, it is not uncommon to feel as though you are being asked to choose between mother and husband or wife.

As you begin the colouring exercise, allow yourself to think deeply about mother. Give yourself space to consider the many implications the word has for you: as a child, for yourself as a mother, for the part of yourself which acts as 'mother' to you. How good are you at taking care of yourself? How well were you taken care of? Is the image you have formed within you of mother a positive or negative one? Whether your feelings are comfortable or confused, it is still useful to examine your relationship with mother.

As you embark on a guided imagery exercise imagine yourself to be in the rich, fertile landscape of the Empress. Feel the hot sun beating down as you stand near the cool waters of the waterfall. Smell the different scents of the meadow and observe the many varieties of plant and vegetation. Approach the Empress now and strike up a dialogue with her. Record your fantasy once you have completed it.

Name:

Date:

Place:

Your key colour:

Notes and observations about your colouring/guided fantasy exercise:

THE EMPEROR

Mythological reference: Zeus
Divinatory meaning: A need to make something solid, to concretise an idea, to build something with a firm structure.

The Emperor, portrayed as Zeus, was ruler of Olympus, the high dwelling place of the gods. He reflects the essence of masculine energy, the driving impulse to create, to impart form and structure. His energy is forceful, dynamic and life-giving, unlike the Empress whose femininity is much more gentle, receptive and preserving. The Empress provides the fertile soil, the Emperor the divine life-giving seed. She is Mother and he is Father. The Emperor symbolises the aspect in man which pushes him to build material constructions and make his creations solid. He guides the ambition which drives us to strive and to succeed. In families, it is often the father who lays down the ideals, morals and aspirations of the family.

THE EMPEROR

As you set out to explore the image of the Emperor in more depth and embark on the colouring exercise, consider your own relationship with father. How do you feel about him? Was he a lenient, helpful, informative, encouraging figure, or was he harsh, authoritarian and rigid? As with the Empress-mother exercise, discovering deep feelings about your personal relationship with father may be comfortable or not, depending, as always, upon your personal experience. But no matter how loving or oppressive your relationship was, there comes a time when you must become your own person, become a capable individual. Separation from mother and father is, as we have seen, a crucial stage of development. Yet the myth of Zeus and Cronus, like that of Demeter and Persephone, shows that separation is not easy. Persephone reaches a compromise with partial separation but Zeus was obliged to dispose of his father completely, in order to free himself from the rigid dictates of that dominating figure. This took him no less than ten years to accomplish. Myth thus tells us that such family conflicts are archetypal and each of us needs to undergo similar struggles in whichever way one's life pattern dictates. Fortunately separation from father does not usually involve literally disposing of him although it can feel just as traumatic.

Use the colouring exercise to explore the various faces of the father, Zeus, allowing your personal experience to guide you. Be aware of your wider associations too, because these connect your general attitude to authority with your relationship with father. Choose a key colour which sums the card up for you and as always keep a note of all the feelings which working on the image evokes.

When you come to do your guided fantasy exercise imagine yourself to be on the top of the icy mountain peaks. It is cold on the mountain top and the colours of blues and purples are cold too. The Emperor is an impressive figure seated on his throne of power and majesty. Approach him and engage in conversation. What strikes you most about the feelings evoked by your meeting with the Emperor? Record your fantasy exercise as soon as it is completed.

Name:

Date:

Place:

Your key colour:

Notes and observations about your colouring/guided fantasy exercise:

THE HIGH PRIESTESS

Mythological reference: Persephone

Divinatory meaning: Thirst for knowledge of an esoteric nature, secrets to be revealed, potential abundant but as yet unfulfilled.

Dream fantasy intuition

The card of the High Priestess depicts Persephone leaving behind the daylight world of her mother, Demeter. The underworld represents what psychology calls the unconscious, that part of ourselves with which we are least familiar even though its influence on our personality is great. The twilight world of which Persephone is queen can be the fruitful and rich womb which holds many secrets until they are ready to be born into the daylight domain of Demeter. The only way to enter Persephone's realm is through dreams, fantasies and intuition. Demeter rules the day while Persephone rules the night.

THE HIGH PRIESTESS

As you colour in Persephone's image, think about your own attitude to self-discovery. After all, discovery has two sides to it: some of the treasures hidden in the unconscious may be pleasant, others not so pleasant. The black and white pillars at the entrance of the underworld reflect the duality of both creative and destructive impulses, hidden in the unconscious mind. The High Priestess is an image representing vast potentials as yet unfulfilled, and secrets yet to be revealed. Her domain is like the hidden world of the womb which silently provides protection until its precious seed is ready to be given life. Persephone protects thoughts, feelings, memories and dreams until they are ready to be released into consciousness.

Persephone rules the feminine world of night, sleep and dreams. As you begin to examine this side of your personality in greater detail you can start to contact Persephone's essence. She is subtle and fascinating but we cannot understand her meaning by using our conscious rational minds. She reveals her secrets gradually and cautiously: we usually get glimpses of her meaning through the world of dreams. Consider your associations with the dream-world and the unconscious mind. Do you think dreams are meaningful or merely a useless clutter of images? Does the idea of trying to make contact with the unconscious frighten or excite you? C. G. Jung, the great Swiss psychologist, likened the dread and resistance which every human being feels when it comes to delving too deeply into himself, to the fear of the journey to Hades and the underworld. Notice the kind of colours this image requires you to choose. Find a key colour which sums up the elusive essence of the High Priestess.

When you embark on your visualisation exercise, try to feel the sensation of leaving behind the warm sunshine. Imagine yourself to be descending with Persephone down those damp clammy steps into the depths of the musty dark underworld. Strike up a conversation with Persephone. Perhaps you could ask her how she feels about her dual role as Princess of the Day and Queen of the Night. See if you can recognise a similar duality in yourself. Make a careful record of the various feelings, thoughts, sensations and impressions which emerge as a result of your fantasy encounter with the High Priestess.

Name:

Date:

Place:

Your key colour:

Notes and observations about your colouring/guided fantasy exercise:

THE HIEROPHANT

Mythological reference: Chiron
Divinatory meaning: Need for spiritual purpose, the search for a personal philosophy, or spiritual values.

The Hierophant image depicts Chiron, the King of the Centaurs, a race of creatures who are half man and half horse. The Hierophant is an image of the quest for spiritual satisfaction and meaning in life. His quest for greater understanding of the inner world is more direct and straightforward than that of the mysterious High Priestess, whose elusive world is not penetrable by the intellect alone. The Hierophant's energy is masculine, outgoing and assertive, like his earthly counterpart, the Emperor. The Emperor and the Empress make up the earthly parents of the conscious mind and material world, while the Hierophant and the High Priestess symbolise the spiritual parents of the unconscious inner world. The union of the earthly Emperor and Empress brings forth a physical child; the union of the celestial Hierophant and High Priestess produces the spiritual one. The combination of masculine and feminine produces a third entity. This process occurs within the psyche as well as literally.

The Hierophant is the spiritual teacher who seeks to find a connection between the world of men and that of the gods. He is a bridge builder, forging the link between our material and spiritual worlds. Thus the ancient word 'pontifex', or maker of bridges, was used to designate a priest. Chiron is not an orthodox priest, however, and does not represent orthodox religions. He lived in a cave, not a temple, and his instruction on spiritual understanding does not consist of dogma,

THE HIEROPHANT

but rather of bringing each individual pupil to his own encounter with the divine.

As you consider the image of the centaur Chiron and begin your colouring exercise, think about your attitudes towards religion, orthodox or otherwise. What does God mean to you, if anything? It is helpful to reflect upon your spiritual upbringing or lack of it, and to allow yourself to ponder its validity or lack thereof. Try to determine which of the values instilled in you by background or upbringing are truly appropriate for you. Unlike the High Priestess, the Hierophant offers many alternatives and choices which can be considered on an intellectual as well as spiritual level. In other words, the Priestess' realm is one of dream, fantasy and intuition, which cannot be clearly perceived by the conscious mind. The Hierophant, in contrast, is accessible through word, book, lecture or service. The options open to us are set out more lucidly and we can thus begin to formulate our own personal philosophy.

As you colour the Hierophant's image notice how your choice of colours reflect your own thoughts about spirituality. Choose a key colour which can sum up the essence of the Hierophant for you. When you embark on your guided fantasy exercise imagine yourself to be with him in his cave. Start your conversation with the Hierophant. What does he say to you? As always record your thoughts and impressions when you have finished the exercise.

Name:

Date:

Place:

Your key colour:

Notes and observations about your colouring/guided fantasy exercise:

THE LOVERS

conscious decision making (handwritten)

Mythological reference: The judgement of Paris
Divinatory meaning: A love affair with a trial or choice attached.

Choices that stem from the heart (handwritten)

THE LOVERS

The image of the Lovers reflects Paris, who was called upon by Zeus to judge a beauty contest between the three great goddesses, Hera, Athene and Aphrodite. It is worth noting the various choices Paris was offered: power and wealth by Hera, victory in battle by Athene, love and beauty by Aphrodite. While it may be understandable that Paris, as a young man, opted for love and beauty, it is also clear that he did not consider the options carefully nor did he give a thought for the consequences of his choice. When making choices in life we often tend to go for the option which has the most obvious advantages, not realising that there may be adverse consequences as well. Every choice has both advantages and disadvantages connected to it. Sometimes it is wise to consider not what has the greatest advantage but what has the least disadvantage.

The card of the Lovers follows from the Fool's discovery about the complexity of his parenthood. As you come to study the Lovers in more detail, bear in mind what the previous exercises concerning mother and father have revealed. Try to connect your own romantic choices with your experience of relationships within your family. The way you regard relationship will inevitably have been affected by the kind of relationship you had with your parents and they had with each other. The choices that were made in your family will obviously have bearing on the choice you make. The world of love and relationships which the Lovers represent requires particular kinds of choices to be made. Paris as a young man is more concerned with his physical desires than their consequences. So, too, the first relationships we form in adolescence tend to be based on the physical magnetism of the other partner, not on his or her deeper qualities of character. As we become more mature, however, other factors such as compatibility and positive qualities of character assume equal importance.

As you begin to colour in the image of the Lovers, allow yourself time to think about your own attitudes to love. What is important to you in a relationship? How do you pick partners? On what do you base your choices – physical appearance, wealth and status, quality of character, friendship or passion? Select key colours for this card; colours which sum up both its bright and dark side.

When you start the visualisation exercise put yourself in Paris' shoes. Imagine you were faced with such a choice. How would you handle it? Imagine yourself standing on the mountainside with the delicate task of giving a precious prize to one of the three goddesses standing before you. have several conversations if possible, one with each goddess, asking advice, and one with Paris asking his reasons for his choice. You might like to ask each one of them a specific question regarding a choice you have to make. As usual make a note of all that took place in your fantasy visit to the land of the gods.

Name:

Date:

Place:

Your key colour:

Notes and observations about your colouring/guided fantasy exercise:

THE CHARIOT

Mythological reference: Ares
Divinatory meaning: Conflict within, struggles and battles, but potential for victory, resolution of quarrels.

THE CHARIOT

The image of the Chariot represents Ares, the god of war. His chariot is drawn by two strong horses who appear to be intent on pulling in opposite directions. The Chariot is an image of inner struggle between the various different parts of the personality. We are made up of many feelings, thoughts and notions which may tug in different directions. Whenever we feel torn inside, perhaps wanting to do something we feel guilty about, the image of the Chariot with its horses pulling in opposite ways, may be conjured up. The horses, one black, the other white, symbolise these differences. Each seems intent on getting its own way, even if this means splitting the chariot asunder. It is the job of the charioteer to maintain control, to take hold of the warring impulses and curb them. Kahil Gibran says that your soul is like a battlefield upon which reason and judgement often wage war against passion and appetite. 'I would have you consider your judgement and your appetite even as you would two loved guests in your house. Surely you would not honour one guest above the other; for he who is more mindful of one loses the love and faith of both.'

The message of the Chariot is that all opposites can stand side by side. The identity of each is made more distinct by virtue of its opposing characteristic. Without conflict, there is no progress, for it is the conflict in our lives that induces us to change and grow. The conflict makes us dissatisfied with our present way of living and encourages us to find new solutions. Were we free of conflicts, we might never risk the challenge of moving onwards and upwards to a higher level of life.

As you colour in the image of the Chariot, try to recognise the opposites within yourself. Identify the emotions which give you the most trouble and imagine them as 'loved guests in your home'. See how they could co-exist without exalting one at the expense of the other. Allow the many contradictory thoughts, feelings and desires to exist together within. Each must be allowed full expression, because war will break out if the inner forces struggle for recognition while you try to deny their existence. Realise that you can be both cowardly and courageous, weak and strong, that you can contain love and hate together in your heart. Like the two steeds that draw the Chariot, one black, the other white, so must the negative and positive impulses that comprise your nature be made plain. Allow yourself to explore the contradictory feelings. Choose a key colour to sum up this card's essence and think about the way you settle inner conflicts.

When you start on the guided fantasy exercise imagine yourself to be on a battlefield. The air is hot and dusty and the noise of battle a dull roar in the distance. You are standing with the charioteer and together you try to control the wild horses. Talk to Ares, the god of war. Note all the thoughts and feelings that come from the conversation.

Name:

Date:

Place:

Your key colour:

Notes and observations about your colouring/guided fantasy exercise:

JUSTICE

Mythological reference: Athene
Divinatory meaning: Need for clarity of mind, impartial judgement, and a balanced intellect.

JUSTICE

The image of Justice portrays the severe, wise and beautiful goddess Athene. She is seated in a cool-looking throne room with everything around her perfectly balanced. Athene was a warrior goddess but she did not employ the brute force of the war god Ares. On the contrary, she fought her battles with strategy and skill. Thus she balanced Ares' aggression with logic and mental agility. Hers was the power of the intellect, of mental alertness and skill, and those she favoured had to display similar qualities. As well as her function as warrior goddess, she was venerated as goddess of the arts, of peace, and as goddess of prudent intelligence. Her emblem was the wise owl.

The Justice card concerns the ability to discriminate and make choices based on dispassionate, impersonal evaluation of merit. The Lovers card dealt with choices that stem from the heart. Justice, on the other hand, requires impartial evaluation of a situation. Athene gives the ability to think conceptually. Justice is essentially a human concept which inspires in mankind the hope of attaining a better life. Justice involves fairness, using the intellect as arbiter. Life is not fair, nor is nature fair. Nevertheless, man at his best does strive towards fairness, and Justice is his attempt to establish equilibrium as a guiding principle in the world and in society. The achievement of this ideal is, of course, ultimately impossible because reality and nature cannot be 'tamed' by man. Nevertheless constant striving for Justice is considered to be one of the most noble manifestations of the human spirit.

Justice exemplifies Athene's high principles and her need to fight for noble causes. Justice represents the uniquely human quality of impartial judgement and the power of the rational mind. It is this faculty which separates man from the animal kingdom. Although we share instinctual drives with the animal world, we possess another dimension, that of rational conceptualism.

As you prepare to colour the Justice image, allow yourself to consider how your mind functions. Is it easy for you to be objective or do you tend to view life subjectively? Is it easy for you to be rational? How do you think; logically, or emotionally? Are you influenced by personal desire? Let these and other questions of your own pass through your mind as you choose your colours. Pick out a key colour which sums up the Justice card for you. Justice reflects the positive need for a balanced mind but an impassive intellect can shut out compassion and mercy.

When you attempt the guided fantasy exercise imagine yourself to be entering the hall of Justice. The room is light and airy but with a cool atmosphere. It is very still and quiet and as you approach the Justice figure notice how calm and balanced she is. Start a conversation with the goddess Athene. As always make a careful note of the meeting as well as the thoughts, feelings and associations evoked by the exercise.

Name:

Date:

Place:

Your key colour:

Notes and observations about your colouring/guided fantasy exercise:

TEMPERANCE

Mythological reference: Iris

Divinatory meaning: Harmony within relationships, co-operation resulting in happy marriage or partnership.

The image of Temperance portrays the goddess of the rainbow, the gentle Iris. She was a messenger of the gods, especially to Zeus and Hera, and was loved by gods and men alike because of her kind and willing nature. She was equally at home in the sky, the earth and the sea. Even the underworld would open at her command. The flowing curves of the Temperance image stand in contrast to the austere and symmetrical lines of Justice. As Justice is strictly fair so Temperance is compassionate and merciful. Justice stands for the thinking function while Temperance stands for the feelings. Iris, or Temperance, is depicted pouring water from one cup to another, symbolising the need for continual flow and movement of feeling to prevent stagnation. The cups she uses to keep the flow of feelings constant are of gold and silver. Gold is the metal of the sun or the masculine, and stands for consciousness; silver is the metal of the moon or the feminine, representing the unconscious. The realm of feeling is volatile and changeable, although not always gentle. Amicable Iris could also display anger, and exacted Hera's vengeance when necessary. Temperance requires that the flow of feelings, whether angry, disappointed, hurt or loving, must be maintained. The feeling nature is changeable and often as unpredictable as the sea itself: one day grey and menacing, the next shining blue and clear. Your feeling nature will often give rise to conflicting needs. These may

TEMPERANCE

not lend themselves to impartial evaluation yet they must also retain a balance. You will know from your own experience that undue weight given to any feeling over another will inevitably injure them all. Just as the mind must strive to achieve a rational balance, so must the emotional heart.

As you begin to colour the image of Temperance, think of the shifting, changing subtlety of the rainbow's hues and see how they reflect the ever-changing realm of your own feelings. As you carefully select the colours, including one key colour, let your feelings flow. See how many different emotions you can evoke in yourself by thinking of different situations: some which make you feel happy, some which make you feel sad. See if there are certain feelings which you are consciously aware of denying. Explore your emotions by considering the things you desire and the things that you dread. Notice how your feelings mix and blend, just as water flowing from one cup blends with that in another.

When you proceed with your visualisation exercise, imagine yourself to be standing in the emerald green meadows filled with irises. Imagine the soft fresh atmosphere just after a rainfall and see the emergence of a rainbow. Before you stands the goddess of the rainbow, her robes intermingling with the water in the pool at her feet, her rainbow wings merging with the delicate colours of the rainbow itself. Talk to the goddess and make notes of the details of the exercise.

Name:

Date:

Place:

Your key colour:

Notes and observations about your colouring/guided fantasy exercise:

STRENGTH

Mythological reference: Hercules

Divinatory meaning: Need for strength, courage and self-discipline. Potential for moral victory and mastery of life.

The image of Strength depicts Hercules in combat with the Nemean Lion. The fight resulted in a kind of union between the man and beast, with Hercules assuming the beast's impenetrable skin for protection. The message this card contains is that we need to tame the demanding self-centred beast within us and bring the power to good use.

The lion represents the powerful, passionate side of the human psyche, which may make itself apparent in a number of ways. It may be totally repressed or it may be allowed to rule the personality totally. It may be controlled, mastered and integrated, or it may wantonly destroy. The lion is a royal beast and contains the positive elements of dignity and leadership. When opposed, however, it can be highly dangerous and destructive. The lion within us is represented by the childlike demand for everything to go our way and by the rage evoked when things do not. A healthy balance in childhood comes when the will is tamed but not broken. In a sense, Hercules does this by destroying the dangerous, violent, destructive parts of the lion while proudly honouring its useful aspects, as embodied in its resistant skin.

The child whose will has been broken may feel unable to establish true control or mastery over his life. He can feel unworthy or unable to strive for what he desires. He may feel he does not deserve to have what he desires. On the other hand, the child whose inner 'lion' has never been tamed will

STRENGTH

continue to ride roughshod over whoever gets in his way. He will have no regard for the needs or feelings of others and will behave like the Nemean Lion, devouring whoever crosses his path. The trick lies in confronting one's natural desire and finding a way of utilising it creatively. A steady inner development of courage, strength and self-discipline is needed to integrate the powerful elements within, so that they are neither crushed underfoot nor allowed to dominate all else.

As you set out to work colouring this image, think about your own associations with power and mastery. Are they familiar to you? Is the lion in you crushed or rampant? Have you found the point at which you can use your beast creatively? What was your experience of early childhood? Were you allowed to roam freely or were you over-restricted? How do you go about getting what you want in life? Through covert manipulation or overt aggressive tactics? As you colour the image let these questions drift through your mind and see how the colours you choose relate to the feelings this image evokes. Choose a key colour which can sum up this card's meaning for you.

When you are ready to start the visualisation exercise, imagine that you are in the dim-lit lair of the Nemean Lion, watching Hercules as he fights bare-handed with the ferocious beast. When the lion is slain, talk to Hercules about his victory. Once you have concluded the exercise make notes as usual.

Name:

Date:

Place:

Your key colour:

Notes and observations about your colouring/guided fantasy exercise:

time
healing
vov~8/5

THE HERMIT

Mythological reference: Cronus

Divinatory meaning: A time for withdrawal, silent meditation and solitude. Patience is needed to confront one's inner world.

The image of the Hermit is sombre. Cronus is depicted amid a lonely landscape carrying the scythe of time and the lamp to gain insight and understanding from the solitary period of waiting to which he has been subjected. The salutary message of the Hermit is that of accepting the limitations of time and old age. Whether we like it or not, and Cronus apparently did not, we must all grow old. We may attempt to deny or disguise the ageing process with paint and dye, but time has no regard for cosmetics. The myth warns us that if we do not accept the limits imposed by time, a worse fate will befall us. Uranus and Cronus refused to pay attention to the demands for new life as symbolised by their sons, and both were ignominiously deposed. By refusing to accept the inevitability of the end of their reign, Cronus and his father Uranus before him, were violently overthrown by their children.

Among the lessons which the Hermit has to teach us are those of acceptance and patience. The bright light of his lamp symbolises the illumination of the inner world when the outer one seems dark. But the Hermit can also teach us about solitude. One of man's greatest fears is that of being alone. However, having submitted yourself to that test, you can discover the resources that solitude can confer. In order to be able truly to join another, you must first be truly alone yourself. Otherwise the union is born out of fear of solitude and simply becomes a crutch.

THE HERMIT

When solitude is confronted and in turn accepted, it is no longer so frightening. It releases us to make decisions which need not be based on the fear of isolation.

As you begin the colouring exercise, dwell for a quiet moment on your own attitude to old age, time and solitude. Be patient with yourself and give yourself enough time to meditate on this, for the Hermit gives the best results when contemplated at leisure. Examine your feelings about old age. Do you fear growing old or are you able to let go of each stage as it loses its potency? Examine your attitude towards solitude. Do you enjoy or fear it? Choose the colours which seem appropriate to reflect your feelings about the Hermit. Choose a key colour which sums up his essence and meaning for you.

When you start your guided imagery exercise imagine yourself on a darkening lonely plain. The land is flat with the hint of mountains far in the distance. Dusk has fallen and it is nearly night. Towards you walks a solitary figure, dressed in dark robes, his face half hidden by his cowl. He carries a lamp which lights the area around him and sends out rays of warmth and comfort despite the gloom surrounding him. Walk towards him and stand by his side. Allow yourself to remain silent with him for a while, to feel the effect of his solitary presence. If appropriate talk to him, if not simply remain quietly at his side. The time and effort you put into this exercise will be worthwhile.

Name:

Date:

Place:

Your key colour:

Notes and observations about your colouring/guided fantasy exercise:

THE WHEEL OF FORTUNE

Mythological reference: The Moirai

Divinatory meaning: Change in fortune, new beginnings, a new chapter in life starting. The Wheel makes a new turn.

THE WHEEL OF FORTUNE

The image of the Wheel of Fortune depicts three women, the spinners of fate, known collectively as the Moirai. The Wheel of Fortune represents life woven and then measured out differently for each man. At the same time, however, it is also what, in some deeply mysterious way, each man chooses. The image of the wheel itself is one of fixed stability commingled with change. As the rim of the wheel revolves, external circumstances and situations change but the centre remains stable. Our true Self is symbolised by the quiescent hub which does not move but causes the outer rim of the wheel to turn. Just as the rim and hub are both parts of the same wheel, so human fate and human soul are one and the same. You are thus responsible for your own destiny. Your fate does not come to meet you. On the contrary, you go to meet your fate.

When joy or sorrow comes into your life, it is not that fortune or misfortune has befallen you, but rather that you have invited it into your life. Everything in the outer world exists within the hearts and souls of each of us. It is our fear of recognising our own responsibility for the course of our lives that leads us to try to blame fate for what befalls us. The more we know, therefore, about the inner Self which attracts external circumstances to us, the more power we can consciously exercise over our destiny. Many people do not like the idea of such responsibility; they prefer to think their circumstances have nothing to do

with them and ascribe everything to good or bad fate. The Wheel of Fortune, however, reveals a greater force working within, an intelligent and orderly plan behind the seemingly random changes in one's life. The three spinners are part of the unconscious within each of us, and we choose, on some profound level, the course our life will take.

As you prepare to colour in the mysterious image of the Wheel of Fortune, examine your own attitude towards fate. How do you see it? How much responsibility are you willing or prepared to take for your life's course? Using hindsight, can you see that certain times in your life which seemed unnecessarily terrible had a strange meaning and maybe a value. 'Much of our pain is self chosen,' says Gibran. 'It is the bitter potion by which the physician within you heals your sick self. Therefore trust the physician and drink his remedy in silence and tranquillity ...' As you colour the image and find a key colour which calls to mind this card's essence for you, allow yourself to ponder these complex matters.

As you embark on the visualisation exercises, imagine yourself to be in the dark cave with the three spinners. Notice how they spin, measure and cut, and as they do so watch the Wheel in the centre turning. See how the figures rise and fall. Turn to each of the spinners and talk to them about their task. Talk to them about the thread and fabric of your life. Record the feelings these mysterious women stir in you.

Name:

Date:

Place:

Your key colour:

Notes and observations about your colouring/guided fantasy exercise:

THE HANGED MAN

Mythological reference: Prometheus
Divinatory meaning: A sacrifice must be made to gain something of greater value, time in suspension.

The Hanged Man shows an image of the Titan, Prometheus, hanging upside down from a rock. Prometheus loved mankind dearly enough to steal precious fire from the gods, with which he sought to enlighten humanity. Because of his love for the human race, he was prepared to make a painful sacrifice in order to obtain the holy fire.

THE HANGED MAN

Sacrifices can be made for one's own wishes, for the sake of the community or for mankind at large. But whatever the sacrifice may be, it will consist of voluntarily giving something up for something which is of greater value to the person, cause or country. On an inner level, the journey to the underworld of the unconscious can involve giving up the power of the conscious mind in order to gain greater knowledge of the unknown. Many mythic heroes or gods, including Hercules, Theseus, Odysseus and Orpheus made the journey to the underworld in order to return with a lost treasure reclaimed. This involved the risk of not returning at all, for the journey to the underworld was notoriously perilous. Any sacrifice requires a risk or an act of faith because there are no guarantees of success.

The Hanged Man appears in the archetypal journey at a point when the hero, the Fool (or oneself) begins to realise that there is more to life than what is visible on the surface. The first half of the journey, as in the first half of life, is concerned with external matters: freeing oneself from childhood patterns, coming to terms with one's parents, relationships, educations and careers. The Hermit then appears as a reminder that life is not infinite; limitations exist and must be recognised. The Moirai give us more responsibility for our own destiny and the Hanged Man marks the point at which the conscious mind has, as C.G. Jung puts it in *Psychology and Alchemy*, volunteered to die in order to beget a new and fruitful life in that region of the psyche which has hitherto lain fallow in darkest unconsciousness, under the shadow of death.

As you prepare to colour in the image of the Hanged Man consider the implications of the Prometheus myth. Can you think of a time when you had to make an important sacrifice? How did you feel about it? Is there an important sacrifice to be made at the moment? How can you let the image of Prometheus guide you? There is a choice to be made, a conscious voluntary choice which will inevitably have far-reaching consequences. How prepared are you to take on the responsibility? Did you learn anything from the Wheel of Fortune about assuming responsibility for your own destiny? All these questions will increase the depth of your understanding of this ambivalent image.

When you proceed to your guided fantasy imagine yourself hanging upside down. How does the world look from this different perspective? Join Prometheus on his lonely rock and talk to him about his sacrifice. Talk to him about your own. Record your impressions of this fantasy exercise.

Name:

Date:

Place:

Your key colour:

Notes and observations about your colouring/guided fantasy exercise:

DEATH

Mythological reference: Hades
Divinatory meaning: The end of something which has been lived out, transformation, new beginnings to follow.

DEATH

In the card of Death, Hades is portrayed dressed in black robes, receiving gifts from people kneeling before him. Death in the Tarot does not connote physical death. On the contrary, it means that a cycle has ended and a new one is ready to begin. However, the transition between death and new life requires a period of mourning, like the coin that must be paid Hades to gain entry to the underworld. If we refuse to accept that a real ending has occurred, we do not mourn the loss and thus cannot symbolically let the soul rest. By acknowledging and mourning losses or endings, we can let things end peacefully and clear the way for a new beginning. If the ending is not accepted, a new beginning cannot take place. In most cultures, any period of change is marked by an initiation ceremony or particular ritual. In some cultures today, puberty, the moving out of childhood into adulthood, is marked with a feast, or with some trial which must be completed in order to cross the bridge. In most of the western cultures, however, the transition into puberty goes unannounced and unnoticed. Marriage, birth and death are still accorded certain rituals, but many have lost their deeper significance. For instance, 'stag nights' and 'hen parties' have become an excuse for a party rather than an opportunity for the groom or bride to mourn with their peers the passing away of single life before being ready to accept their new roles.

Failing to mourn the old status before wel-coming the new can leave couples unaccountably depressed on the wedding day or honeymoon. They do not realise that this feeling arises because they have failed to pay Hades his coin. They have not entirely recognised what they have given up and so cannot fully embrace the new. Parenthood is another beginning at which failure to recognise the end of the carefree old way of life and mourn its passing can result in depression. It might have something to do with our society's lack of willingness to accept any negatives. We prefer to concentrate on the 'isn't it lovely?' side of marriage or birth, but do not like to look at the loss which needs to be mourned.

As you begin to colour in the image of Death, think about your own attitudes to change, endings, new beginnings, death of the old and rebirth of the new. How do you react when things change? How do you cope with loss? Do you allow yourself to mourn, or do you prefer to block out the sadness? Use your choice in colours to reflect your mood and choose a key colour which can sum up Death for you.

In fantasy prepare to cross the River Styx. Once in the kingdom of Hades, confront the dark figure, dressed in black robes with a death mask covering his face. What does he say to you? Can you talk to him? How do you feel? It is cold in the underworld, and a mist is rising from the leaden river; yet on the other side the new dawn is breaking. A new day is about to begin.

Name:

Date:

Place:

Your key colour:

Notes and observations about your colouring/guided fantasy exercise:

THE DEVIL

Mythological reference: Pan
Divinatory meaning: A confrontation with the inner world. Facing fears and inhibitions can foster growth.

The image of the Devil shows a figure, half man, half goat, playing pipes in a dark cavern. On an inner level Pan is a symbol of the side of ourselves that we least like. We would prefer to be able to hide our unpleasant side for fear of being shunned by others, just as Pan was shunned by the other gods for his ugliness. Pan, who symbolises among other things the primitive hidden instincts in man, also represents all desires which, in their base manifestations, are greedy and lustful. He is the fuel that feeds the desires which the lion displayed in the card of Strength. The lion was to be found in an open-mouthed cave which at least made him accessible. Pan, however, resides deep in the bowels of the earth, or the unconscious. He cannot be reached except with much difficulty. He represents the shadow side of the psyche which contains all the aspects of our personality we would rather not know about. The first and easiest way to discover these aspects is to examine the people we most detest. Whatever qualities we most dislike in them are sure to be lurking within us, in that deep cavern ruled by Pan.

The Devil signifies blocks and inhibitions, usually sexual, which hinder growth and cause power to be misused. But he also indicates that if the blocks can be removed great progress can follow. By transcending the fear and shame which keep us tied to the Devil, much positive energy can be regained. As we begin to face our shadow, taking

THE DEVIL

responsibility for the aspects within us we dislike, we will feel less hateful or contemptuous of others who display similar qualities. The more we can accept ourselves as having lustful, greedy, destructive elements to our personality, the more we can accept other people's faults. If we deceive ourselves, believe that we are faultless and that only others are venal, we open the way for the dark side of our nature to gain power. This may occur insidiously and without conscious consent, for that which is not allowed natural expression may resort to covert, devious and twisted expression. A powerful example of how the shadow may gain control is seen in the way that Hitler and his Party attributed to the Jewish people everything that was unpleasant and evil, while extolling the virtues of the Aryan race as everything light and good. The result of this is well known.

As you contemplate the Devil image and begin to colour it, consider your associations with the shadow side of man generally and yourself in particular. What do you know about the dark side of your nature? Choose a key colour which sums up the Devil's essence.

When you embark on your visualisation exercise, imagine yourself to be in a dark, enclosed space, like a cavern in the depths of a mountain side. There is a damp, earthy smell perhaps faintly goatish. The space is hot and airless. In this place you encounter the Devil, Pan. Talk to him and the people who stand in his power.

Name:

Date:

Place:

Your key colour:

Notes and observations about your colouring/guided fantasy exercise:

41

THE TOWER

Mythological reference: The slaying of the Minotaur.
Divinatory meaning: Breaking down existing forms, changing false structures and finding true values.

The image of the Tower struck by lightning from Poseidon's trident is a powerful one. The Tower is the only man-made image in the Tarot and as such represents the constraints of society's demands and the strict requirements of convention. Sometimes we are so afraid to commit a wrong in society's eyes that we commit a wrong to ourselves instead. We are so ashamed of our shadow that we build a persona or labyrinth within to hide it. We then find ourselves in the unhappy position of having to put more energy into the disguise than anything else. Minos found himself having to slaughter more and more of his innocent subjects in order to keep the Minotaur fed. Psychologically, we do the same by using up more and more of our energy to keep secrets of which we are ashamed. The myth reflects what happens when we hide from the truth and refuse to confront our own transgressions. It may start with a small lie that grows and grows until it forms a tangled complex web, and the disguise starts to cause more discomfort than the lie itself.

In the myth, the hero Theseus at last found his way into the labyrinth, using a magical golden thread as talisman to light his way. He slew the Minotaur and freed Crete. When we make the perilous journey into the unconscious, we need a talisman too. It is often a therapist who can help us enter this dark world, providing us with the insight into our problems, just as Ariadne gave Theseus the

THE TOWER

magical twine to help him on his way. Once the beast has been tracked down and rendered harmless, we no longer need hide behind elaborate structures, and human sacrifice need not be made. The Minotaur, like the Devil, is connected with a sexual secret concerning bestial origins, which must be hidden from the eyes of 'polite society'. As we become increasingly aware of how much we are betraying our true selves, we start to welcome the bolt of lightning which destroyed the labyrinth completely: divine inspiration from the god Poseidon. We, too, need to break down unhealthy structures in ourselves.

When you start to colour the image and find a key colour, ask yourself what sort of structures you use to hide the parts of your psyche of which you are ashamed. Try to think about the areas you hide from yourself, discover which parts of your psyche you are disguising and why. See where your efforts to disguise your true self hinder your progress.

As you prepare to do the guided fantasy exercise, imagine you are present with Poseidon as he sends the lightning and thunder which destroy the Tower. Perhaps you could imagine yourself, as Theseus, entering the dark labyrinth of your own unconscious, using a golden thread to guide you. What sort of a Minotaur do you discover? How do you go about slaying it? Let your imagination go in the fantasy exercise, always remembering to note your impressions and feelings about it carefully.

Name:

Date:

Place:

Your key colour:

Notes and observations about your colouring/guided fantasy exercise:

THE STAR

Mythological reference: Pandora's Box
Divinatory meaning: Hope, inspiration, faith and belief in a new and better life.

The image of the Star is that of Pandora opening her fateful box and, despite the escape of all the ills, Hope remains. The Star of Hope symbolises the magical side to the human spirit which never gives up believing in a better world. No matter how despairing, no matter how dismal, when we have hope we can carry on. During grave illness, doctors sometimes say, 'He has given up hope', and the fight for life is lost. Bruno Bettleheim sadly observed during his time in a concentration camp, that once the light of hope went out of his fellow prisoners' eyes, it was only a matter of days before they died. The Star has been a symbol of hope and promise for many centuries. Sailors used the stars to steer their course at night, the Wise Men followed the Star of Bethlehem to find Jesus. We 'thank our lucky stars' and 'wish upon stars' today. The hope and inspiration which the Star in the Tarot represents is vital for keeping a sense of equilibrium, particularly when life is at a low ebb. Without the special sense of faith and unquenchable hope of the Star, we, in dire circumstances, simply wish to stop living.

Everyone needs a goal to believe in, and while that goal is alive within, anything is possible. If we stop believing and lose hope that things can improve, the light goes out in our hearts and ultimately in our lives. The Star is, therefore, an extremely important stage of the journey to understand and integrate. Our own attitudes to hope are crucial to how we live our lives, how we treat ourselves and

THE STAR

others. If we do not respect our own lives, why should we feel any different towards anyone else's? But if we do cherish and appreciate life, our attitudes begin to change. It is often when we are in danger of losing something that we begin to appreciate it, and that which we appreciate we cherish.

As you prepare to colour the Star image, think about your own reactions in difficult, painful circumstances. Is your first instinct to give up or is it to keep fighting, hoping, believing? What associations and feelings does the image of Pandora opening the forbidden box evoke in you? Note your colour choice, paying special attention to the key colour.

As you proceed to the guided fantasy exercise, imagine you are Pandora. Imagine for an instant that the world is a beautiful, unsullied place, where no evils or ills exist – a perfect place. Now imagine opening the lid of a chest that you have been warned not to open. As you do so, out fly all the Spites which plague mankind: old age, labour, sickness, insanity, vice and passion, and spread over the world. Only Hope remains. Turn your gaze to the Star of Hope. What words does she have to offer you? Can she offer you something to strengthen your own sense of faith and hope? Does Hope have inspiration to give you which you can use to keep on believing in life's goodness? See what this fantasy exercise evokes in you and as always make careful notes and records of each attempt.

Name:

Date:

Place:

Your key colour:

Notes and observations about your colouring/guided fantasy exercise:

THE MOON

Mythological reference: Hecate

Divinatory meaning: Fluctuation, uncertainty, confusion. Time of passivity rather than action.

(handwritten: like the ocean) *(handwritten: unconscious)*

THE MOON

The image of the Moon shows the triple-headed lunar goddess Hecate. Hecate, who ruled the dark side of the moon, is the mistress of darkness and ruler of the night, during which man returns to the womb of sleep, to slumber and dream. The Moon's three phases are reflected in the image of Hecate as the three faces of the feminine; the virgin, the mother and the old crone. They also symbolise the stages in life: youth, middle age and old age. The Moon presides over all things connected with the feminine archetype, including the menstrual cycle, which lasts for approximately twenty-eight days – the same time it takes for the Moon to complete its three phases. The ancients believed that the Moon contained the souls of the unborn as they waited for life, and that the dead were gathered up to her womb to wait for rebirth. It thus became an image for the Great Mother, from whom all life springs and to whom all life returns. The world that the Moon card symbolises is boundless and deep. The ocean is an apt image to consider when trying to understand the vague and constantly shifting world of feelings, which the Moon embodies. The ocean's depths contain many secrets, and many of its deepest beds are still unreachable to man. The ocean can be friendly one day, cruel the next. Sailors know that they can never presume to 'tame' the sea, for such power and might elicits respect, not arrogance. We might use the same analogies to comprehend fully, or to make conscious all its contents. We know there is a wealth of information contained in the unconscious but, like the sea, some of its depths can never be fathomed. The best mediums we have to gain access to our inner world are dreams, fantasies and art. Like the High Priestess, the Moon is not an easy card to understand. The exercises are therefore vital.

When contemplating the Moon card and preparing to colour its image, let your thoughts wander around the subject of dreams, day-dreams, emotions and fantasies. Try to imagine what the ocean within yourself is like. Let your imagination play around motifs of water, waves, foam and what might be contained at the bottom of the sea within you. Once again, let your choice of colours roam freely and notice which colours you are drawn towards. Choose a key colour which can sum up the essence of this card.

When you embark on your visualisation exercise imagine yourself to be at the edge of a deep dark pool. Imagine the swirling mists arising from the pool; feel the cold damp night on your skin. Try to conjure up the smell of night-time as you stand by the pool. Before you appears a figure, a woman. She is the Moon, with its three faces. Address a question to each of her aspects: the virgin queen, the mother and the mistress of magic and darkness. Note all the associations, feelings and thoughts which arise in connection with this fantasy exercise.

Name:

Date:

Place:

Your key colour:

Notes and observations about your colouring/guided fantasy exercise:

(handwritten margin note: need b/b/bro ✓ moon + sun)

THE SUN

Mythological reference: Apollo
Divinatory meaning: Optimism, time of positive action, energy in abundance, a time of clear vision.

THE SUN

The image of the Sun stands in sharp contrast to the grey and silver Moon card, for Apollo, the brilliant Sun god, appears in shimmering gold. In the Tarot, the Sun rules the day, and offers a time for positive energy and clear perception. The Sun represents the masculine energy which gives form and structure to dreams or fantasies. The Moon represents the inner feminine archetype of Mother, while the Sun reflects the outer masculine archetype of Father. The polarity between the Sun and Moon is that of form and formlessness. The Sun symbolises consciousness, the Moon the unconscious. Each is necessary for balance both within our own psyches, and within the cosmos of which we are, after all, a part. The warm generous Sun ripens the grapes in the vineyard, but also produces the cruel heat that can shrivel the earth, and create barren deserts. The Moon controls the water which we need for life, but water can also cause destructive floods. If you approach the Sun with reverence and respect, he will prove a benevolent source of life. But if you approach in arrogance and pride, you may meet with danger. The Sun's fiery energy is a creative source of strength, warmth and light. He bestows clarity of vision, creative inspiration and artistic talent in abundance. He is the masculine principle embodying much outgoing, positive energy, unlike the Moon, whose energy is indrawn and passive.

The balance between day and night, sun and shadow, light and dark, positive and negative, is a delicate one which we must learn to integrate and respect in order to achieve a sense of inner calm. We must learn to use both the Sun and the Moon within, for each has its unique and invaluable lessons. Without a balance, one or the other would exercise a disproportionate influence, becoming destructive and overpowering. The Sun and the Moon need each other, in equilibrium, in order to confer their positive gifts.

As you prepare to colour in the image of Apollo, the Sun god, choose the colours which call to mind the message he brings you. Choose a key colour which sums up the essence of the Sun, and think about the gifts of artistic and creative resources he can offer. How does this reveal itself in your own creative expression? What sort of feelings does the Sun evoke in you? Do you welcome his warming rays or feel overwhelmed by his brilliance? Think about the contrast between the Sun and Moon. Try to feel their balance within you.

Proceeding to your guided fantasy exercise, imagine yourself standing before Apollo. The heat of the sun is at its height and the sky is brightest blue. The shining vision of Apollo stands before you. What do you want to say to the Sun god? What does he have to say to you? Note your feelings evoked by this exercise and then compare them with your feelings towards his counterpart, the Moon. Note carefully all the various associations that spring to your mind.

Name:

Date:

Place:

Your key colour:

Notes and observations about your colouring/guided fantasy exercise:

JUDGEMENT

Mythological reference: Hermes, the Psychopomp
Divinatory meaning: Time for reaping rewards for past actions, time for reaching conclusions and summing up situations.

JUDGEMENT

The image of Judgement depicts Hermes in the role of Psychopomp, guide of all dead souls. In this role, Hermes was the underworld guide who summoned the dead and led them to their final reckoning. At the end of the journey through the Major Arcana, Judgement symbolises the appointed time in a phase or cycle when a summing up of the process is required. All the experiences gained during the journey through the Major Trumps are revalued and examined. This is the time at which actions, decisions and choices are looked at with the benefit of hindsight, to see which decisions were sound and which faulty. In other words, it is the moment for reaping the harvest and deciding, by examining the crop, which fruits did well on certain soils and which did not. We are well rewarded for the choices which were sound and fruitful, but are required to pay the price for ill-chosen decisions. The Judgement card reveals the time for this final stage of purification and transformation, before the completion of the journey.

The figures rising from the coffins reflect your past selves, your past values, which you must now confront and judge. Three figures represent a continuum of past, present and future. Judgement marks the final resolution, the completion of the karmic cycle whereby you must reap what you have sown. Imagine yourself to be on a stage, taking part in a play. When you can look upon each of the players through the eyes of all the other characters; when you can understand each one and can play each part, only then can you truly understand the play which is your life. Each of the figures of the Major Arcana plays a part in your life: each of them is part of you. In reviewing your journey through the cards, you must review your part in the various situations in which you have found yourself throughout your life. As you progress to understand all the characters and the play itself, you become one with the author of the play, yourself.

When you start to colour the card of Judgement, think about the exercises you have done, and what you have learned about yourself through the Major Arcana. Think about any situations in your own experience which you might associate with this card. What feelings does it evoke? Which colours do you choose to reflect those feelings? Choose a key colour which sums up the Judgement card for you. Is your inner judge merciful and kind or harsh and overbearing?

As you embark on your penultimate guided fantasy exercise, imagine yourself being summoned by Hermes the Psychopomp and led to your own judgement. How would your progress be evaluated? Where have you succeeded and where have you failed? Perhaps you can imagine being judged on your performance so far in learning the deeper meanings of the Tarot cards. Make a note of all the thoughts and feelings stimulated by this exercise and see what you have achieved so far.

Name:

Date:

Place:

Your key colour:

Notes and observations about your colouring/guided fantasy exercise:

THE WORLD

Mythological reference: Hermaphroditus
Divinatory meaning: Success, achievement, attainment, the realisation of a goal or the completion of a cycle.

The final image of the Major Arcana, the World, portrays a curious figure dancing inside a golden oval. The figure is of a hermaphrodite, symbolising the unity and perfection to be gained when all the lessons have been learned and are balanced. The final stage of the journey results in the unification of all opposites: masculine and feminine, dark and light, positive and negative. The four symbols in each corner stand for the four elements from which the world is supposedly composed, reflected in the four suits of the Minor Arcana, the Cup, the Wand, the Sword and the Pentacle. The four elements have fused to form a perfect fifth, symbolised by the central figure: man as a fully integrated being. The figure is protected by the golden snake devouring its own tail, the symbol of eternity. The journey never really ends, because at the moment of completion, a new cycle begins.

THE WORLD

The World card stands for the peak of attainment, the reward for all effort, the crowning glory. But even in that wonderful moment of triumph, there is the knowledge of a new goal to be attained. The World is perhaps one of the most abstract images in the Tarot, and is therefore a difficult one to comprehend fully. The World dancer assembles the cast of reality in a festive dance, turning all creation into a celebration and a unity with its creator. The dance is the journey through the Tarot, and as you dance, you become one with it. The dance and dancer fuse to enter a close circle of completion, thus becoming one with the World and its Creator. This is the dance of the history of mankind. To attain your place in the World card is to know everything, forgive everything and love everything. When you arrive at this true understanding, all becomes lovable in the totality of the World. Most of us, of course, will not manage to attain such perfection. But every time we satisfactorily complete something that we have worked hard for, the World is conjured in a moment of triumph and joy. It stands for reward as one cycle has been successfully completed.

As you begin to contemplate and colour the World image, think over the journey you have made through the Major Arcana. What have you learned? What have you gained? What have you lost? Has it changed you at all? If so, how? Choose a key colour which sums the World up for you and make a note of the feelings which arise as you colour in.

When you proceed to make your final visualisation exercise, imagine yourself floating in space, just like the World dancer. You are in the clear blue sky, amongst the clouds, lighter than a bubble. Join the World dancer in the golden circle and see if you can strike up a conversation with the strange, two-headed figure. In this card you find the end and the beginning. You can, therefore, repeat the journey as often as you like, each time finding something new and different in the images of the Major Arcana to help you grow and develop.

Name:

Date:

Place:

Your key colour:

Notes and observations about your colouring/guided fantasy exercise:

General Exercises

Now that you have completed your journey through the Major Arcana and worked on the colouring and guided fantasy exercises, lay the twenty-two Major Trumps before you on a table. Let your thoughts wander at random as you contemplate each of the twenty-two images.

Allow yourself time to consider them all. As you contemplate the various images, see which cards appeal to you most, and which evoke a sense of fear. Now select a card which awakes a particular anxiety in you. Consider the image closely and try to identify what it is that makes you afraid. Go back over the text for the card, checking on your own notes and observations. When you have identified and in some way confronted the unease that this image inspires, choose a card which you find reassuring or comforting. Seek out an image which can assuage your sense of anxiety. As before, try to determine what especially reassures you about this image. Once again, review the text and your own notes about the cards, recognising the reasons for your choice. Write down your discoveries in the section provided.

Repeat this exercise with a card which is attractive and gives you a sense of confidence. Try to identify the particular qualities which you find most inviting. Then seek out a card which strikes you as unattractive or repellant.

When you have established what it is that causes your dislike, make notes on these cards in the space provided.

Now choose a card which could act as a personal significator, a card which most reflects your own individuality. For example, can you identify with the assertive masculinity of the Emperor, or the illusive feminine qualities of the High Priestess? Then choose another card which most nearly represents your anti-self, the card which raises your most alien and uncharacteristic attitudes. Do you feel you lack the optimism of the Star, or the wisdom of the Hermit? Take time to explore these images.

Next, take the three pairs of opposites and lay them in a pattern in front of you. Which of these cards would you most like to adopt as your inner teacher? Which card could function best as a guide to your discovery of yourself through the Tarot?

Now look at the twenty-two Major Arcana again as a whole. Ask yourself which cards you feel you understand the best. Make a note of them. Now ask yourself which cards you feel the least affinity with, or have the most trouble in understanding. Make a note of these too. Try to identify in the images the qualities that make them either easy or difficult for you to relate to. Write down your findings in the space provided.

Why not experiment using this exercise with a friend or fellow Tarot student?

Date:

Comfort card: Its key colour:
Reason:

Fear Card: Its key colour:
Reason:

Attractive card: Its key colour:
Reason:

Repulsive card: Its key colour:
Reason:

Your personal significator card: Its key colour:
Reason:

Your anti-self card: Its key colour:
Reason:

Inner teacher card: Its key colour:
Reason:

Inner guide to Tarot: Its key colour:
Reason:

Notes on the connections between colours and cards:

Notes on the Major Arcana as a whole:

ASTROLOGY AND THE COURT CARDS

This section discusses the correlation between the Court cards – Page, Knight, Queen and King – and astrological sun signs, elements and qualities. Astrology uses the four elements of Water, Fire, Air and Earth to reflect various ways of expressing energy: Water reflects feelings and emotions, Fire symbolises imagination and creativity, Air is connected with the intellect and the capacity to think, while Earth is associated with the body and its material needs. The four suits in the Minor Arcana encompass the many aspects of life's experiences using a similar model. Thus, Cups are connected to Water and feelings, Wands relate to Fire and imagination, Swords are associated with Air and thinking, while Pentacles are connected with Earth and the material world. The Pages, which are not related to any astrological sign, indicate the potential contained in each of the four elements. They are not included in the zodiacal diagram opposite but they introduce the element into each suit.

Astrologically there are twelve signs of the zodiac, three of which are assigned to each element. Water encompasses Cancer, Scorpio and Pisces; Fire encompasses Aries, Leo and Sagittarius; Air encompasses Gemini, Libra and Aquarius; and Earth encompasses Taurus, Virgo and Capricorn.

Another important classification of the astrological signs is represented by three qualities, known as Cardinal, Fixed and Mutable which reflect three basic principles of life: creation (Cardinal), preservation (Fixed) and destruction (Mutable). Each phase of life is born, lives and dies, or changes in order to be born again.

The Cardinal signs generate outgoing dynamic, forceful energy. The four Kings are connected with the Cardinal signs as they are authoritative, powerful and full of energy to organise. They reflect the Cardinal creative, enterprising ways of relating to life, with a strong will to accomplish goals and realise ambitions. The Cardinal signs in astrology are Aries, Cancer, Libra and Capricorn.

The Fixed signs are more consistent, persistent, loyal and reliable, with great reserves of patience. The four Queens are connected with Fixed signs and are images of stability, receptivity and containment. They share the qualities of loyalty, reliability and capacity to nurture also relevant to the Fixed signs of Taurus, Leo, Scorpio and Aquarius.

The Mutable signs are easily adaptable, flexible and volatile, always ready and willing to change to suit the current mood or surrounding environment. The four Knights are connected with the Mutable signs as they are always seeking new goals and challenges. They share the characteristics of adaptability and volatility common to the Mutable signs of Gemini, Virgo, Sagittarius and Pisces.

The diagram opposite shows how the division between signs, elements, qualities and Court cards is made. You will see that there is one sign for each element in each quality represented by a Tarot Court card. Careful thought should be given to these distinctions and through the exercises given in this chapter you will find that linking the Tarot with astrology yields fresh insight into the meanings of the cards while the myth of each card gives a new perspective on our personalities by way of the zodiacal sun signs.

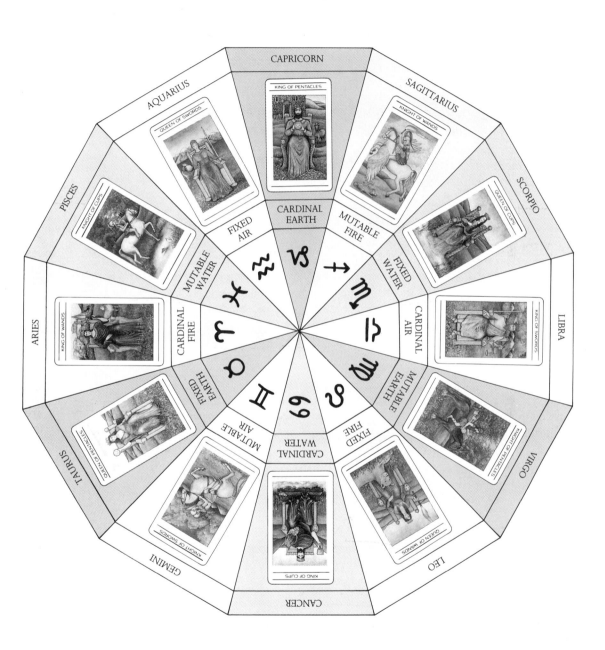

messengers

PAGE OF CUPS

Element: Water Mythological reference: Narcissus
Divinatory meaning: Birth of new feelings, fragile new beginnings in the world of emotion.

PAGE OF WANDS

Element: Fire Mythological reference: Phrixus
Divinatory meaning: The bearer of good news, a desire or stirring of creative growth.

The Page of Cups portrays a boy gazing in rapture at his own reflection; he is the youth, Narcissus. The suit of Cups is connected with the element of Water, which is in turn associated with feelings, and by extension relationships. It encompasses the many-faceted nature of emotion and the suit is therefore expressed through myths of relationship. The Page of Cups is the messenger who brings the fragile beginning of self-love. On the face of it, the Narcissus myth appears rather destructive. Nevertheless it does reveal the importance of first being able to love oneself before one is able to love another. Psychology uses the term 'narcissism' to describe the first months of an infant's life in which he or she is totally self-absorbed. If the infant can feel loved and accepted by his environment, he builds up an inner picture of his own lovableness and worth. He can then move on to perceive the same qualities in others. If the early experience is unsatisfactory he may remain fixed in self-preoccupation and as in Narcissus' case, it may prove his undoing.

The Page of Cups conveys the message that time and space must be provided for new feelings to grow and develop. When the Page of Cups enters your life, you may be sure that a new phase is approaching in which your 'feeling' world must be developed and brought to maturation. It may come through a new relationship with another, or it may be evoked by the birth of a child. Think of situations from your own experience.

The Page of Wands depicts a boy, the mythic figure Phrixus, riding triumphantly upon a golden ram, bearing a flaming wand aloft. The element of Fire connected with the suit of Wands embodies positive qualities of artistic talent and flair, imagination and creative ability. Fire is also volatile and unpredictable, yet it can warm cold hearts and lighten dark places. The element of Fire symbolises that part in us which spurs us on to meet challenges, explore the realms of our imagination, and develop the creative and artistic potential dormant within. Fire, like imagination, can transform and change substances without altering itself and thus reflects the imagination at its most creative. The Page of Wands is the messenger who brings new ideas, and so forms the basis for new ventures to begin. Just as Phrixus brought the treasured Golden Fleece to Colchis, thus setting the stage for Jason's great adventure, so the small beginnings connected with creativity, imagination and inspiration will be ready to unfold when the fiery Page of Wands appears.

The Page of Wands indicates the beginning of a new phase, in which your creative world must be developed and given a new lease of life. The messenger may come in the form of an inspirational or artistic person entering your life, or perhaps an opportunity will arise for you to develop creative talents through career or study. Think of a situation from your own experience which might be reflected by the Page of Wands.

PAGE OF SWORDS

Element: Air Mythological reference: Zephyrus
Divinatory meaning: Beginnings of intellectual development;
gossip or idle talk may cause disruption.

PAGE OF SWORDS

The Page of Swords portrays a young man seated upon a cloud, the mythic Zephyrus. The element of Air is connected with the suit of Swords, and with the mind. Thus Air is the most human element. It is unique to mankind which has the capacity to think abstractly and form concepts. The double-edged quality of the suit of Swords is apt for this element, as the mind can impose logic and coherence upon the most incomprehensible situations, yet can also cut and cause harm with its sharp, inflexible edge. The Page of Swords can be seen as the messenger who carries ideas and thoughts, thus providing the basis for new intellectual concepts to flourish. Initially, as is the tendency with some children, Zephyrus, god of the West Wind, appears cruel and malicious when in the company of his brother, the North Wind; he inclines towards unkind gossip and deceit. As he grows up, however, he develops a far more pleasant, reasonable side: the positive qualities of Air, which are just, fair, logical and reasonable. Zephyrus does not remain malicious forever, but tempers his personality in time.

When the influence of the Page of Swords enters your life, you will know that a new phase is about to begin in which your rational mind must be developed. This may come through an intellectual person, or it may unfold as a conscious desire to develop the abstract or conceptual side of your personality to greater capacity. Think of related situations from your personal experience.

PAGE OF PENTACLES

Element: Earth Mythological reference: Triptolemus
Divinatory meaning: Beginning awareness of the value of
material sense; slow and patient development.

PAGE OF PENTACLES

The Page of Pentacles portrays a young boy, the mythic figure Triptolemus, standing in a field of green plants and new seedlings, carefully holding a golden pentacle. The element of Earth is connected with the suit of Pentacles, which in turn represents nature, the body, and all things material. Unlike the fluid element of Water, changeable Fire, or the volatile element of Air, Earth is stable and changes slowly within its destined time. It cannot be hurried any more than nature and natural growth patterns can move outside their cycles. To understand this element is to understand physical laws, the needs of the body, the needs which require a solid framework in which to house the other, more volatile elements. The Page of Pentacles is the messenger who carries ideas of an earthy nature which may form the basis for new material capabilities to unfold. As with all the Pages, the beginnings are slow, vulnerable and fragile, but they contain great potential. The Page of Pentacles suggests that interests, skills or talents can be brought slowly but surely to fruition, given sufficient time, patience and effort.

When the influence of the Page of Pentacles falls upon your life, your material sense must be developed. This may come through a practical earthy person who influences you, or it may come through your own need to develop such qualities within. Think about a situation from your personal experience which reminds you of the Page of Pentacles.

KNIGHT OF CUPS

Pisces (February 20–March 20)   Element: Water   Quality: Mutable
Mythological reference: Perseus

KNIGHT OF CUPS

The Knight of Cups is portrayed as a handsome, gentle-looking man, clad in silver fish-scale armour and crowned with a fish-tail, while a fish, the symbol of Pisces, leaps out of the water at his horse's feet. In order to appreciate the quality of the Knight of Cups, it will help to understand something of the sun sign Pisces. As we have seen, the quality of both the sign and the card is mutable, as are those of all the Knights, for in essence they are volatile and changeable. The mutable signs never stay the same for long; they adapt easily to any circumstances and are willing to change, chameleon-like, to suit the atmosphere and needs of others around them. Pisceans are by nature feeling types, which means they act and react according to how they feel rather than what is logical. They tend to be idealistic, romantic and sensitive, as well as self-sacrificing. They will sacrifice a great deal in the name of love. Pisceans love to be in love. They are romantic about everything, especially love affairs. Every aspect of life must contain some element of romance for them. Otherwise they become bored and lose interest. Although it would require a volume to do justice to each sign, the general characteristics of Pisces are those of kindness, peace-loving and being responsive to the woes of others. Pisceans are great champions of the underdog. Pisceans are frequently generous-hearted, sympathetic and understanding, although their sensitive natures can induce irascibility and a strong tendency towards moodiness. In their most positive light, Pisceans appear resourceful, inspirational and imaginative; but each sign, and Tarot card, has its negative, and the Piscean can also be nebulous, fanciful and lacking in cohesive identity. The Knight of Cups, who is described by the mythic character Perseus, has a lot in common with Pisces. Perseus was the hero who fought not for the glory of battle, nor for his own sense of challenge, but rather for the love of women, thus earning the special favour of the goddess Athene. Perseus sacrificed a great deal in the name of love, first for the love of his mother which sent him on the quest to kill the Gorgon Medusa, and then for the love of Andromeda, his future bride, whom he rescued from the clutches of a fearsome sea monster.

The appearance of the Knight of Cups in a reading means that the spirit of romance is about to enter your life, either as an upsurge of romance within you, or through a person who encompasses the qualities of 'romantic lover or seducer', and who in turn, awakens romance in you. Think about the sign of Pisces and try to feel the mutable quality of this Watery sign. Consider whether the Perseus myth applies, if only in part, to any Pisceans you know, or to yourself if you happen to be a Piscean. Write down your personal impressions of the sign and what you like or dislike about it in the panel opposite. Now write down your feelings, thoughts and associations about the Tarot image. How do you see the energy of the Knight of Cups manifesting within you? How can you use his energy? Which of his qualities would you most, or least, like to acquire?

Date:

Your own zodiacal sign:

Describe the characteristics of anyone you know born under Pisces:

How do you relate to Pisces in general?

Identify this card with someone you know who conjures up for you the essence of the Knight of Cups:

How do you feel the myth of Perseus matches up to what you know and understand of Pisces?

What do you most admire and like about Pisces and the Knight of Cups?

What do you least admire?

How would you describe the relationship between the card, sign, element and myth?

Have a conversation in fantasy with the Knight of Cups and note the important points:

KNIGHT OF WANDS

Sagittarius (23rd November to 21st December)   Element: Fire   Quality: Mutable
Mythological reference: Bellerophon

The Knight of Wands portrays a handsome, daring young man riding a splendid winged horse. He carries a quiver of arrows over his shoulder, symbol of Sagittarius, the Archer. In the Knight of Wands we see Sagittarius in evidence through the spirit and enthusiasm characteristic of the mutable Fire sign. The mutable quality manifests itself in Fire as a perpetual search for new challenges and new battles to fight. In the Water sign of Pisces, the quest was for love, while in Fire the quest is for adventure, excitement and action. The Sagittarian is by nature intuitive and imaginative, but often out of touch with the limits of reality. Like the Piscean, Sagittarius finds any restrictions extremely tiresome. He is full of wonderful ideas and creative visions, but putting them into practice is a chore which he prefers to leave to other people. Sagittarians often make good teachers and philosophers, for they enjoy lending their opinions to others, but they dislike being told what to do themselves. While the positive qualities of Sagittarius include generosity, creativity, enthusiasm and love of life, the negative qualities include a tendency to be dogmatic, opinionated and unnecessarily tactless.

The Knight of Wands is well described in the myth of the hero Bellerophon, a dashing young man whose enthusiastic, fun-loving nature gained him many admirers, but also brought him a certain amount of trouble. He accidentally killed two men and then sought sanctuary with King Proetus, whose wife fell in love with his charm. Although Bellero-phon rejected her advances, King Proteus was convinced Bellerophon had seduced his wife and suggested that he attempt to slay the Chimera, a mission the king believed would end in death. Bellerophon, assisted by the winged horse Pegasus, was successful in his mission, so he decided to outdo himself and visit Olympus upon his flying horse. This arrogance angered the gods and Zeus sent a gadfly down to sting Pegasus' rump. Bellerophon tumbled ignominiously back to earth.

Bellerophon's enthusiasm and need for ever more challenge is similar to the *cri de coeur* from many Sagittarians. They love to seek new goals but having attained them, they only want to seek others, even more glorious. If the Knight of Wands appears in a reading it means that the spirit of adventure is about to enter your life. This may signify a move of home or country, or it may infuse a spirit of enthusiasm and vision in you through a person possessing such qualities. These will, in turn, be stimulated within you. Think about the sign of Sagittarius and try to feel the mutable quality of this Fiery sign. See if the Bellerophon myth applies, if only in part, to any Sagittarians you know, or to yourself if you happen to be Sagittarius. Write down your personal impressions of the sign, and what you like or dislike about it. Now write down your feelings, thoughts and associations about the Tarot image. How do you see the energy of the Knight of Wands manifesting within you? How can you use his energy? Which of his qualities would you most like and least like to acquire?

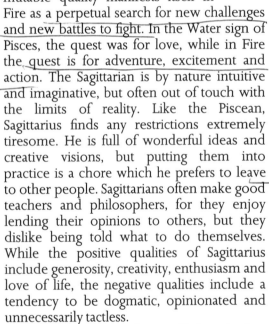

Date:

Your own zodiacal sign:

Describe the characteristics of anyone you know born under Sagittarius:

How do you relate to Sagittarius in general?

Identify this card with someone you know who conjures up for you the essence of the Knight of Wands:

How do you feel the myth of Bellerophon matches up to what you know and understand of Sagittarius?

What do you most admire and like about Sagittarius and the Knight of Wands?

What do you least admire?

How would you describe the relationship between the card, sign, element and myth?

Have a conversation in fantasy with the Knight of Wands and note the important points:

KNIGHT OF SWORDS

Gemini (22nd May to 21st June)   Element: Air   Quality: Mutable
Mythological reference: Dioscuri

The Knight of Swords is portrayed as a set of identical twins, both seated upon a swift-moving horse. The Knight of Swords reflects the mutable Air sign of Gemini, whose symbol is the Twins. The mutable quality of Air expresses itself through a search for communication and new concepts. Geminians are very quick thinking, versatile, vivacious and adaptable, constantly changing their minds and ideas about everything. Because of their penchant for continual change and movement, they are likened to the butterfly which flits between many different flowers, never remaining still for long. Variety is essential for a Gemini, and every day he discovers a new passion which can easily be replaced tomorrow. In relationship, he is like the Sagittarian Knight of Wands, a highly attractive figure because of his mercurial energy, his eagerness to discover and communicate, and his stimulating company. His light-hearted, carefree manner is endearing, but emotional relationships are not always simple with Gemini, who hates emotional scenes and loathes being tied down for any length of time.

The Dioscuri make a good image for the mutable Air sign Gemini. They were warrior twins, one son mortal and the other divine. During battle the mortal twin, Castor, was killed. His divine brother, Polydeuces, was so stricken with grief that Zeus, their father, permitted them both to spend their days alternately in the heavens and the underworld. He set their image among the stars as the constellation Gemini. The continual movement between the heavens and the underworld is an apt image for the mercurial quality to be found in many Geminians. The Knight of Swords is reflected in the mythic figures of the Dioscuri. He likes to be constantly on the move, gathering new ideas and concepts as he goes, most of which he abandons as quickly as he embraces. He is quite likely to persuade, cajole and plead for a particular cause one day, and do a complete turnabout the next.

When the Knight of Swords appears in a spread he heralds a time in which the quicksilver qualities of communication and mental development will stand out. Because of the fluctuating nature of the Twins, the card can also augur a time for sudden changes which disrupt the normal pattern of life. It is likely to present a mind-expanding, progressive period; but the everyday aspects of existence may be led to disarray. This may occur through changes within, or through the appearance in your life of an individual who possesses these Geminian qualities. Think about the sign of Gemini and try to feel the mutable quality of the Air sign. See if the Dioscuri myth applies, if only in part, to any Geminians you know, or to yourself if you happen to be Gemini. Write down your personal impressions of the sign and what you like or dislike about it. Now write down your feelings, thoughts and associations about the Tarot image. How do you see the energy of the Knight of Swords manifesting within you? Which of his qualities would you most like and least like to acquire?

Date:

Your own zodiacal sign:

Describe the characteristics of anyone you know born under Gemini:

How do you relate to Gemini in general?

Identify this card with someone you know who conjures up for you the essence of the Knight of Swords:

How do you feel the myth of the Dioscuri matches up to what you know and understand of Gemini?

What do you most admire and like about Gemini and the Knight of Swords?

What do you least admire?

How would you describe the relationship between the card, sign, element and myth?

Have a conversation in fantasy with the Knight of Swords and note the important points:

KNIGHT OF PENTACLES

Virgo (24th August to 23rd September)   Element: Earth   Quality: Mutable
Mythological reference: Aristaeus

The Knight of Pentacles portrays a serious-looking young man seated upon a sturdy farm horse, carrying a sheaf of wheat, symbol of Virgo. In the Knight of Pentacles we can see the calm, practical way of dealing with situations typical of the zodiacal sign, Virgo. The mutable quality of Earth manifests itself in a search for industry. The element of Earth is made more versatile through the mutable sign Virgo, and thus provides plenty of different and resourceful ways for the energy to be directed. Virgoans are known to be hardworking, paying great attention to detail. They like to be able to discriminate and scrutinise every possibility before making their selection. The positive qualities of this sign are also apparent in their helpful, unassuming, dependable natures, while their more negative qualities often appear as over-fussiness, fault-finding and indecisiveness. Virgoans are often shy and modest, unwilling to project themselves into the limelight, unlike bright Geminians or Sagittarians. Virgo prefers to work away quietly behind the scenes without too much fuss or attention. Virgoans are methodical, painstaking and industrious, able to master the intricacies of any subject they choose to tackle.

The Knight of Pentacles is reflected in the mythic figure of Aristaeus, who was competent in all agricultural matters but his chief interest was bee-keeping. When all his bees started to die mysteriously, he immediately set out to discover the reason and at length approached the prophetic sea god, Proteus. Proteus was notoriously difficult to capture,

but Aristaeus eventually succeeded and thus earned an oracle. Once Aristaeus had resolved the mystery and made the appropriate amends, a new swarm of bees arose from the carcasses of several sacrificial animals. Having fulfilled his tasks to his satisfaction, Aristaeus founded the city of Aristaeum and died there peacefully, honoured for his wisdom.

The Knight of Pentacles embodies many of the qualities of Virgo, particularly the earthy element of contentment with achievement. While all of the Knights exude qualities of restlessness and changeability, Aristaeus displays humility and seems to be the most contented. He regards his task very seriously, as evidenced by the trouble he takes over a handful of bees, but he is rewarded for his conscientiousness. The appearance of the Knight of Pentacles in a reading means that a spirit of determination and earthy practicality is due to enter your life. This may be through inner qualities of perseverance or through contact with a person possessing such qualities. Think about the sign of Virgo and try to feel the mutable quality of the Earth sign. See if the myth of Aristaeus applies, if only in part, to any Virgoans you know, or to yourself if you happen to be Virgo. Write down your personal impressions of the sign and what you like or dislike about it. Now write down your feelings, thoughts and associations with the Tarot image. How do you see the energy of the Knight of Pentacles manifesting within you? How can you use his energy? Which of his qualities would you most like and least like to acquire?

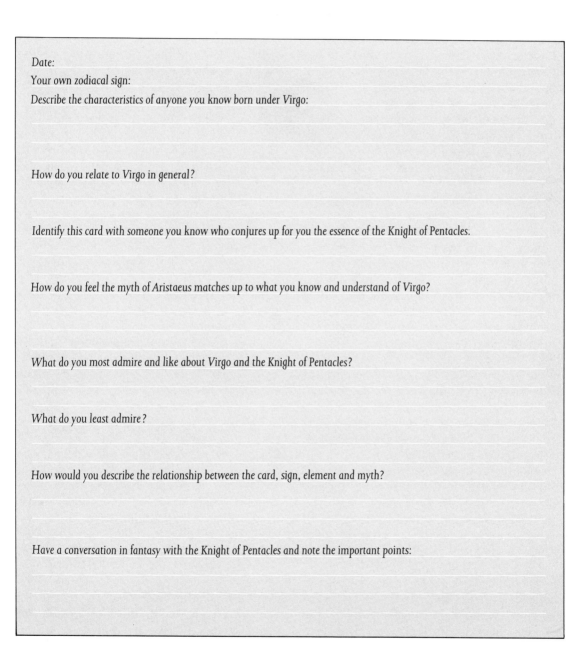

Date:

Your own zodiacal sign:

Describe the characteristics of anyone you know born under *Virgo*:

How do you relate to *Virgo* in general?

Identify this card with someone you know who conjures up for you the essence of the Knight of Pentacles.

How do you feel the myth of *Aristaeus* matches up to what you know and understand of *Virgo*?

What do you most admire and like about *Virgo* and the Knight of Pentacles?

What do you least admire?

How would you describe the relationship between the card, sign, element and myth?

Have a conversation in fantasy with the Knight of Pentacles and note the important points:

QUEEN OF CUPS

Scorpio (24th October to 22nd November)   Element: *Water*   Quality: *Fixed*
Mythological reference: *Helen of Troy*

The Queen of Cups is presented as a beautiful ethereal woman who appears to be merging with the water in which her throne is placed. Golden snakes – the ancient symbol for Scorpio – encircle the arms of her throne. In order to gain a greater understanding of the Queen of Cups, it will help to examine the nature of Scorpio. The fixed quality expresses itself through Water as intense, passionate feelings. Scorpios are well known for their powerful emotional natures. They will hold on tenaciously to what is theirs and refuse to yield anything without a fight. But once a Scorpio loses interest in anything or anybody, the lack of feeling is suddenly and instantly apparent. The quality of fixity is not one which changes easily, and fierce determination can thus reveal itself negatively as ruthlessness. The more positive Scorpio qualities include tremendous loyalty and a sense of responsibility, but their negative aspects can be possessiveness or jealousy, and a tendency to be destructive. Passionately loyal they may be, but nevertheless quite relentless with those who hurt or betray them.

Helen of Troy is an apt image to describe the complex nature of Scorpio, partly because the myth reveals so little about her true emotions. She was a woman endowed with extreme beauty but also a mysterious allure which caused many men to fall hopelessly in love with her. Headstrong and independent, she chose her husband Menaleus, by placing a wreath upon his head, an unusual action for her time, when fathers usually made the choice of husband for their own daughters.

However, when she fell in love with Paris and than eloped with him, the resultant outbreak of the Trojan War apparently did not deter her from following her heart's desire.

The Queen of Cups embodies many of the deep and complex qualities which Helen appeared to possess. She is passionate, proud and intense, refusing to bow to anyone. The Queen of Cups is in command of the depths of her own feeling nature and will act accordingly, not at all concerned about what people think or say. She bases her actions upon what she feels, and that is the most important reality for her.

When the Queen of Cups appears in a spread, the qualities she represents are likely to be brought to the fore. They may manifest themselves through a person entering your life who possesses a strong perceptive nature and a deep desire to learn about the inner world, or alternatively you are nurturing and developing these characteristics yourself. Either way, the time is ripe for discovery of the inner world. Think about the sign of Scorpio and try to feel the stable quality of the Water sign. See if the myth of Helen applies, if only in part, to any Scorpios you know, or to yourself if you happen to be Scorpio. Write down your personal impressions of the sign and what you like or dislike about it. Now write down your feelings, thoughts and associations to the Tarot image. How do you see the energy of the Queen of Cups manifesting within you? How can you use her energy? Which of her qualities would you most like and least like to acquire?

Date:

Your own zodiacal sign:

Describe the characteristics of anyone you know born under Scorpio:

How do you relate to Scorpio in general?

Identify this card with someone you know who conjures up for you the essence of the Queen of Cups:

How do you feel the myth of Helen matches up to what you know and understand of Scorpio?

What do you most admire and like about Scorpio and the Queen of Cups?

What do you least admire?

How would you describe the relationship between the card, sign, element and myth?

Have a conversation in fantasy with the Queen of Cups and note the important points:

QUEEN OF WANDS

Leo (24th July to 23rd August)   Element: Fire   Quality: Fixed
Mythological reference: Penelope

The Queen of Wands is depicted seated upon a throne decorated with lions' heads, with a lioness lying tranquilly at her feet. The lion is the symbol for Leo, astrological correspondent to the Queen of Wands. For a deeper understanding of the Tarot card we must now examine the characteristics of Leo, the fixed sign which expresses the element Fire in a stable, contained way. Fire signs are known to be creative and Leo is certainly blessed with some impressive artistic and imaginative talents. Because of the fixed quality of the sign, Leos seem to manage their strength and energy in such a way as to attain goals and aims more successfully than mutable Fire. Leos are also gifted with organisational ability, particularly in areas where they will earn recognition. Leos thrive on praise and being in the limelight, and are prepared to go to great lengths to achieve credit and public acclaim. They are competitive and like to win, but their greatest attribute lies in their capacity to be intensely individual, while at the same time loyal and generous to those they love. Leo's positive qualities include warmth and sincerity, affection and protectiveness, with an air of genuine self-assuredness. His negative traits include pride, vanity and extravagance with a tendency to show off. No matter how arrogant and bombastic Leo may be, however, his innate optimism and warmth make it hard to be irritated by him for long.

Penelope, the mythic figure who reflects the energy of the Queen of Wands, was the wife of Odysseus. During her husband's long absence at war, Penelope managed their island kingdom single-handedly. She shouldered the task without fuss, having only her young son Telemachus to help her. Although evidently creative and ambitious, Penelope did not waste her resources or energy. She ruled the kingdom wisely as well as remaining a loyal wife to her husband and a steadfast mother to their son. The Queen of Wands presents the admired modern image of a career woman who can still cope easily with running a household, raising children and maintaining a social life. Her tremendous energy is used constructively and within the scope of her capabilities. Unlike the Knight, the Queen of Wands knows her limits and would not try to overstep them. She has intuitive faith in her personal abilities.

When the Queen of Wands appears in a reading the qualities she represents will be ready to fructify. This may occur through contact with a person embodying creative, imaginative and intuitive powers or through the development of these qualities within yourself. Think about the sign of Leo and try to feel the fixed quality of the Fire sign. See if the myth of Penelope applies, if only in part, to any Leos you know, or to yourself if you happen to be Leo. Write down your personal impressions of the sign and what you like or dislike about it. Now write down your feelings, thoughts and associations. How do you see the energy of the Queen of Wands manifesting within you? How can you use her energy? Which of her qualities would you most, and least, like to acquire?

Date:

Your own zodiacal sign:

Describe the characteristics of anyone you know born under Leo:

How do you relate to Leo in general?

Identify this card with someone you know who conjures up for you the essence of the Queen of Wands:

How do you feel the myth of Penelope matches up to what you know and understand of Leo?

What do you most admire and like about Leo and the Queen of Wands?

What do you least admire?

How would you describe the relationship between the card, sign, element and myth?

Have a conversation in fantasy with the Queen of Wands and note the important points:

QUEEN OF SWORDS

Aquarius (21st January to 19th February)   Element: Air   Quality: Fixed
Mythological reference: Atalanta

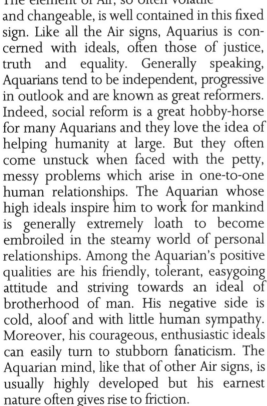

QUEEN OF SWORDS

The Queen of Swords is portrayed as the mythic figure Atalanta, a beautiful but stern woman seated upon a silver throne, pouring water from a jug – symbol of Aquarius, the Waterbearer. In seeking to understand the essence of the card it will help us to look at the energy of fixed Air as manifested through Aquarius. The element of Air, so often volatile and changeable, is well contained in this fixed sign. Like all the Air signs, Aquarius is concerned with ideals, often those of justice, truth and equality. Generally speaking, Aquarians tend to be independent, progressive in outlook and are known as great reformers. Indeed, social reform is a great hobby-horse for many Aquarians and they love the idea of helping humanity at large. But they often come unstuck when faced with the petty, messy problems which arise in one-to-one human relationships. The Aquarian whose high ideals inspire him to work for mankind is generally extremely loath to become embroiled in the steamy world of personal relationships. Among the Aquarian's positive qualities are his friendly, tolerant, easygoing attitude and striving towards an ideal of brotherhood of man. His negative side is cold, aloof and with little human sympathy. Moreover, his courageous, enthusiastic ideals can easily turn to stubborn fanaticism. The Aquarian mind, like that of other Air signs, is usually highly developed but his earnest nature often gives rise to friction.

The myth of Atalanta can help to describe Aquarius and the Queen of Swords. Atalanta was rejected at birth by her father, because he wanted a son, but, adopted by a clan of hunters, she became a fine huntress. She could run faster than any man and equalled many in strength. Upon hearing of her skill, her father decided to acknowledge her and set about finding her a suitable husband. Atalanta refused to marry anyone who could not beat her at a foot race and reserved the right to kill any suitors who tried and failed to win. At last a youth named Melanion consulted Aphrodite, who gave him golden apples to drop during the race. Atalanta, thus distracted, lost the race, but their marriage was alas not destined for happiness. The couple angered the god Zeus by lying together in his sacred grove. In his rage, he turned them into lions; and as the Greeks believed lions only mate with leopards, they were doomed never to couple with each other again.

When the Queen of Swords appears in a reading the qualities she embodies are likely to come to the fore. They may do so in the form of an idealistic, loyal visionary known to you; or they may develop within you. Ponder the sign of Aquarius and try to feel the fixed quality of Air. See if the myth of Atalanta applies, if only in part, to any Aquarians you know, or to yourself if you happen to be Aquarius. Write down your personal impressions of the sign and what you like or dislike about it. Now write down your feelings, thoughts and associations to the Tarot image. How do you see the energy of the Queen of Swords manifesting within you? How can you use her energy? Which of her qualities would you most like, and least like, to acquire?

Date:

Your own zodiacal sign:

Describe the characteristics of anyone you know born under Aquarius:

How do you relate to Aquarius in general?

Identify this card with someone you know who conjures up for you the essence of the Queen of Swords:

How do you feel the myth of Atalanta matches up to what you know and understand of Aquarius?

What do you most admire and like about Aquarius and the Queen of Swords?

What do you least admire?

How would you describe the relationship between the card, sign, element and myth?

Have a conversation in fantasy with the Queen of Swords and note the important points:

QUEEN OF PENTACLES

Taurus (21st April to 21st May)   Element: Earth   Quality: Fixed
Mythological reference: Omphale

the need to take care of oneself

QUEEN OF PENTACLES

The image of the Queen of Pentacles depicts a sensuous-looking woman seated upon a throne decorated with bulls' heads, the symbol of Taurus. In order to better appreciate the Queen of Pentacles we must consider the fixed Earth sign of Taurus. This sign is earthy, acute, and appreciative of both physical and material comfort. Taureans enjoy luxury, beauty and high-quality goods and thrive on anything which pleases the senses. The Taurean nature is basically peaceful, serene and calm although, when goaded, the famous bull-like temper will be aroused. It takes a lot to provoke a Taurean into real anger, but if so provoked, they are more likely to use physical violence than verbal abuse. Taurus signifies patience and perseverence in completing a project. Taureans object to being rushed or pushed; and if they are, the negative side of the sign is revealed: stubbornness and rigidity. When kindly treated, Taureans are steadfast and loyal, loyalty being a quality shared by all the fixed signs. Taureans are by nature practical and patient. They share the quality of contentment with the other Earth signs and once they achieve their goal, they are generally happy and satisfied. If badly treated, however, they will retaliate by becoming unreasonably inflexible and pedantic. Although they love art and beauty and are known for their good taste, Taureans are not generally fired with great imagination or creative vision.

Queen Omphale, the mythic figure used to describe the Queen of Pentacles, was a woman who took great pride and pleasure in physical and sensual comforts. She ruled the kingdom inherited from her late husband and made a wise and powerful sovereign. She was an indulgent woman who lavished the finest silk and perfume goods upon herself. She purchased Heracles, sold as a nameless slave, not as a fighter but as a lover. She had no hesitation in pursuing her sensual desires. Heracles fathered her three sons. They grew up with their father's great strength and aided their mother in running the kingdom. Omphale had a good eye for a bargain and always purchased the best – as exemplified by her acquisition of Heracles. Like Taurus, Omphale possessed the great virtue of generosity.

When the Queen of Pentacles appears in a reading the qualities she embodies are likely to come to the surface. This may be manifest through a meeting with an affectionate, generous, sensuous person, or you may need to develop some of these characteristics yourself. Think about the sign Taurus and try to feel the fixed quality of Earth. See if the myth of Omphale applies, if only in part, to any Taureans you know, or to yourself if you happen to be Taurus. Write down your personal impressions of the sign and what you like or dislike about it. Now write down your feelings, thoughts and associations to the Tarot image. How do you see the energy of the Queen of Pentacles manifesting within you? How can you use her energy? Which of her qualities would you most like, and least like, to acquire?

Date:

Your own zodiacal sign:

Describe the characteristics of anyone you know born under Taurus:

How do you relate to Taurus in general?

Identify this card with someone you know who conjures up for you the essence of the Queen of Pentacles:

How do you feel the myth of Omphale matches up to what you know and understand of Taurus?

What do you most admire and like about Taurus and the Queen of Pentacles?

What do you least admire?

How would you describe the relationship between the card, sign, element and myth?

Have a conversation in fantasy with the Queen of Pentacles and note the important points:

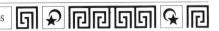

KING OF CUPS

Cancer (22nd June to 23rd July)   Element: Water   Quality: Cardinal
Mythological reference: Orpheus

KING OF CUPS

The King of Cups is portrayed by a dark-haired soulful-looking man seated upon a golden throne with arms decorated by the symbol of Cancer, namely crabs. The cardinal qualities of activity, dynamism and creativity are expressed through the Water element as an overt wish to form personal relationships and help other people. Those individuals born under the sign of Cancer can be instrumental in helping others, particularly in encouraging the growth and development of their emotional potential. Cancer is a very maternal sign, and even the male Cancer is notably motherly, seeking to nurture and protect. Known to be home-loving, Cancerians tend to be adept at creating a comfortable domestic environment. Cancer likes to be needed; and the weaker and more vulnerable you are, the more needed and fulfilled Cancer will be by ministering to you. One of the downfalls of Cancerians is the inability to let go of any person or chattel they consider to be theirs. This results in the negative tendency typical of the sign: a possessiveness and tenaciousness. Relationships are desperately important to Cancerians but although they long for intimacy, their vulnerability in the realm of emotion makes them mistrustful.

Orpheus, the mythic figure chosen to reflect the energy of the King of Cups, was a gentle poet-musician turned priest healer. Orpheus' undoing was his lack of ability to trust. When his beloved wife, Eurydice, was fatally bitten by a snake, Orpheus used all his charms and powers of musical persuasion to gain entry to the underworld and plead for her release.

Finally, the god Hades consented to Eurydice's return to earth on condition that Orpheus led the way and never once looked back until they reached daylight. They were nearly at the end of their long dark journey when Orpheus could bear it no longer and turned back only to see his beloved disappearing, this time forever. Orpheus spent the rest of his days as a priest and healer, tending to the pain and suffering of others. The King of Cups shows a need to understand his own pain, and yet it is so hard to face that he attempts the indirect way so typical of Cancer: he heals himself via healing others. He tries to instil in others the very thing he cannot achieve himself – the ability to trust.

When the King of Cups appears in a reading it means that the qualities he embodies are ready to manifest themselves. This may come through a meeting with a caring, concerned, nurturing person or it may be that you have to develop some of the maternal, protective qualities within yourself. Think about the sign Cancer and try to feel the cardinal quality of Water. See if the myth of Orpheus applies, if only in part, to any Cancerians you know, or to yourself if you happen to be Cancer. Write down your personal impressions of the sign and what you like or dislike about it. Now write down your feelings, thoughts and associations to the Tarot image. How do you see the energy of the King of Cups manifesting within you? How can you use his energy? Which of his qualities would you most like and least like to acquire?

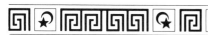 

Date:

Your own zodiacal sign:

Describe the characteristics of anyone you know born under Cancer:

How do you relate to Cancer in general?

Identify this card with someone you know who conjures up for you the essence of the King of Cups:

How do you feel the myth of Orpheus matches up to what you know and understand of Cancer?

What do you most admire and like about Cancer and the King of Cups?

What do you least admire?

How would you describe the relationship between the card, sign, element and myth?

Have a conversation in fantasy with the King of Cups and note the important points:

KING OF WANDS

Aries (21st March to 20th April)   Element: Fire   Quality: Cardinal
Mythological reference: Theseus

The King of Wands is portrayed by a good-looking man seated upon a throne decorated with rams' heads, the symbol of Aries. The cardinal qualities of activity, dynamism and creativity are expressed through the Fire element as a desire for adventure and action. Those born under the sign of Aries are generally outgoing, impulsive and brimful of grandiose ideas. Ariens tend to be enthusiastic and dramatic, always willing to experiment with something new and adventurous. Like the other Fire signs, Ariens have a great deal of childlike spirit; they are full of energy and life; they are easily quelled but will bounce back in no time. Aries has little or no patience and dislikes being bothered with details, such as who might foot the bill for the grand schemes he dreams up. Easily angered, his rage is short lived and grudges are quickly forgotten. Aries will explode in a fit of temper one minute, but will have no recollection of why in the next. He can be bossy, self-centred and opinionated, but extremely generous and basically kind-hearted. Although irritating at times, his exuberant, dynamic spirit can be very endearing. His vibrant energy and ever-ready willingness to embark on adventure is refreshing to the less optimistic. His constant quest for new goals can be exhausting or inspiring to those around him.

Theseus, the mythic figure who represents the King of Wands, is a truly Arien hero. When Crete was under threat from the unquenchable appetite of the Minotaur, Theseus could hardly wait to try his hand at slaying the monster. He set sail in a vessel whose black sails signified mourning for the loss of lives thus far. Theseus promised his father he would change the black sails for white if his mission was successful. In true heroic fashion, with the help of a beautiful maiden, Theseus succeeded in killing the beast but in the excitement of his victory Theseus forgot to change the sails to white. His father, anxiously scanning the horizon for news, saw the black sails and assumed the worst. In despair, he threw himself into the sea. This exemplifies Aries, lack of attention to detail; through no deliberate omission, but by the failure to think of others, Theseus inadvertently caused his father's death.

The King of Wands is a wonderfully Arien character; at best he is warm, generous and charismatic, at worst pushy, irritating and self-obsessed. When he appears in a reading the qualities he represents will become apparent. This may be through meeting a fiery, impulsive, enthusiastic person, or it may mean that you yourself will have to develop some of the optimism and exuberance he possesses. Think about the sign of Aries and try to feel the quality of cardinal Fire. See if the Theseus myth applies, if only in part, to any Ariens you know, or to yourself if you happen to be Aries. Write down your personal impressions of the sign. Now write down your feelings, thoughts and associations to the Tarot image. How do you see the energy of the King of Wands manifesting within you? How can you use his energy? Which of his qualities would you most like, and least like to acquire?

Date:

Your own zodiacal sign:

Describe the characteristics of anyone you know born under Aries:

How do you relate to Aries in general?

Identify this card with someone you know who conjures up for you the essence of the King of Wands:

How do you feel the myth of Theseus matches up to what you know and understand of Aries?

What do you most admire and like about Aries and the King of Wands?

What do you least admire?

How would you describe the relationship between the card, sign, element and myth?

Have a conversation in fantasy with the King of Wands and note the important points:

KING OF SWORDS

Libra (24th September to 24th October) Element: Air Quality: Cardinal
Mythological reference: Odysseus

The King of Swords is portrayed as a dignified fair-haired man holding the symbol of Libra, a pair of perfectly balanced scales. The positive cardinal qualities of activity, dynamism and creativity are represented through the Air element as mental skill, agility and dexterity. Those born under the sign of Libra are known to be diplomatic, lovers of harmony needing a stable balanced environment. Because Libra is an Air sign, those born under it often display a markedly intellectual streak and a love of knowledge. They like to use language exquisitely; and communication is important to them. They are receptive to reason with logic and persuasion. They enjoy working with others and have a very great talent for gaining co-operation in working environments. They enjoy the gift of lucid thinking and clarity of mind, and can express their thoughts felicitously. Although usually diplomatic and seemingly gentle, their minds function rapidly, with subtle penetration behind the engaging exterior. Like all the other Air signs Librans have lofty ideals particularly in the area of partnerships. Libra, though not always noted for compassion and empathy, is a sign known for its decency, and fairness.

Odysseus, husband of Penelope whom we met as the Queen of Wands, is an apt image for Libra. He was known for his cleverness, quick wit and guile. When he joined the Greek expedition against Troy, he proved to have sound advice and good strategic plans. Odysseus managed to talk his way out of many extraordinary situations and charm his way out of the others. He also used his wits in brutal ways during encounters with giants, sorceresses and sirens, who tried to trick him, or lure his crew to their death. Odysseus was always too clever for them, however. He was an ingenious hero, using shrewd words rather than brute force to achieve success.

The King of Swords makes a formidable opponent but a good man to have on your side. He can be maddening in his insistence for fairness and equality and his inability to respond spontaneously to an emotion. If something is put across reasonably enough it will impress the King of Swords. If feelings and emotions are presented in a muddled, incoherent way, they will not interest him in the slightest.

When the King of Swords appears in a reading the qualities he embodies are likely to come to the surface. This may be through an intelligent and charming, high-principled person, or it may mean that you need to develop some of his logic and reasoning powers within your own personality. Think about the sign of Libra and try to feel the quality of cardinal Air. See if the Odysseus myth applies, if only in part, to any Librans you know, or to yourself if you happen to be Libra. Write down your personal impressions of the sign and what you like or dislike about it. Now write down your feelings, thoughts and associations to the Tarot image. How do you see the energy of the King of Swords manifesting within you? What do you want from him? Which of his qualities would you most like and least like to acquire?

Date:

Your own zodiacal sign:

Describe the characteristics of anyone you know born under Libra:

How do you relate to Libra in general?

Identify this card with someone you know who conjures up for you the essence of the King of Swords:

How do you feel the myth of Odysseus matches up to what you know and understand of Libra?

What do you most admire and like about Libra and the King of Swords?

What do you least admire?

How would you describe the relationship between the card, sign, element and myth?

Have a conversation in fantasy with the King of Swords and note the important points:

KING OF PENTACLES

Capricorn (22nd December to 20th January)   Element: Earth   Quality: Cardinal
Mythological reference: Midas

KING OF PENTACLES

The King of Pentacles card is symbolised by a dark-haired man seated upon a fine throne decorated with the heads of mountain goats, the symbol for Capricorn. The strong cardinal qualities of activity, dynamism and lively creativity are expressed through the Earth element as an overt wish to establish a solid relationship with the physical world. Capricorn is a sign which desires status and some position in the world, and social acceptance is therefore greatly important. In realising their ambitions Capricorns are not afraid of hard work and will suffer many hardships to reach their goal. There is a strong sense of determination and a powerful will which eventually takes Capricorn to his desired goal. Whether this goal is money, power or acclaim, he will set out with the utmost resolution to attain his dream. Earth is the element which encourages the desire to fulfil an idea or concept. The Capricorn's greatest talent lies in the field of organisation and control. He is disciplined and structured, wasting no time or resources that are not absolutely necessary. He can also be a great upholder of family traditions, society and the correct way to behave within the context of that family and society.

King Midas is the mythic figure chosen to represent the King of Pentacles. Midas prized money above all else and when Dionysus offered him a wish in exchange for a kindness he had performed, Midas immediately requested that anything he touched turned to gold. He realised quite quickly this was an unwise wish, for he could not eat golden food nor drink wine which became gold. When he broke down in despair and hugged his precious daughter, she too turned to gold. Dionysus, amused but compassionate, freed Midas from his curse but the king continued to remain rich for the rest of his life.

The King of Pentacles is known for his 'Midas touch'. Everything he sets out to do in the financial world seems to make money and he is generally comfortable and well off. He is an image of the side of man which aspires towards material comfort and possessions. As he is an Earth sign, he is generally content once he achieves his goal. Unlike the Fire signs, which constantly seek new challenges, Earth signs relax once the fruit of their labours have been harvested.

When the King of Pentacles appears in a reading the qualities he embodies will become prominent. This may be through a wealthy, ambitious, and materially-oriented person, or you may need to develop some of his ambitions and drive for material gain within. Think about the sign of Capricorn and try to feel its quality of cardinal Earth. See if the Midas myth applies, if only in part, to any Capricorns you know, or yourself if you happen to be Capricorn. Write down your personal impressions of the sign, and what you like or dislike about it. Now write down your feelings, thoughts and associations to the Tarot image. How do you see the energy of the King of Pentacles manifesting within you? How would you use his energy? What do you want from him? Which of his qualities would you most, and least, like to acquire?

Date:

Your own zodiacal sign:

Describe the characteristics of anyone you know born under Capricorn:

How do you relate to Capricorn in general?

Identify this card with someone you know who conjures up for you the essence of the King of Pentacles:

How do you feel the myth of Midas matches up to what you know and understand of Capricorn?

What do you most admire and like about Capricorn and the King of Pentacles?

What do you least admire?

How would you describe the relationship between the card, sign, element and myth?

Have a conversation in fantasy with the King of Pentacles and note the important points:

General Exercises

Lay the four sets of Court cards out in front of you. Try to picture each set as a family. What sort of natural family would each suit make? Imagine the four families as neighbours in a small town or suburb. How do you imagine they would get along together? Which families do you suppose would engender the greatest friction? Which would enjoy the greatest harmony? Let your imagination wander over these questions, and arrive at a solution to the conflicts, using the four Court suits as your main characters. Imagine the dialogue and interaction between all the personalities. Spend as long as you like on this exercise, perhaps writing it as a play or story, adding a little to it each day or week. The fantasy will bring the characters alive in your memory, and should facilitate your interpretation of readings. Indulge yourself in the pleasure of speculation and give yourself maximum freedom in developing whatever comes to mind in this uninhibited study of the sixteen Court cards.

Another exercise is to form a picture of your own family using the Court cards as members. For example, is your mother more like the Queen of Pentacles or the King of Wands? Does your father resemble the King of Swords or the Queen of Cups? Remember that the Kings and Queens do not represent strict sexual gender but rather a quality of personality. Pick out your siblings from the Pages or Knights, perhaps. Can you see any connection between the dynamics of your family and the signs, elements and myths described by the Court cards? Why not write a story about the members of your family using the Court cards as personalities?

Now choose your own personal significator card. Which of the Court cards is most like you? Which would you most wish to be like? Which mythological character do you most identify with? Which do you feel is your alter ego? Looking at the three cards you have selected, your personal significator, the card you would most like to aspire to, and the card which represents your alter ego, how do you see these three interacting? Are you happy with your personal significator or would you like to change something about it? If so, what? How can you reach the qualities in the card representing your most desired qualities? How can you integrate or transform the qualities you least like in yourself? The more time you spend on these exercises, the more you will learn about aspects of yourself you did not know existed.

It can prove helpful and interesting to discuss this exercise with a friend or colleague. Let each of you choose cards for one another and compare the cards you choose for yourself with the ones chosen for you. Such interaction can produce new ideas.

If you have a particular interest in astrology and know something about your natal horoscope you could pick out the appropriate card for your Sun, Moon and ascending signs. For example, if you are Taurus with Moon in Scorpio and Libra rising, your Court cards would be Queen of Pentacles, Queen of Cups and King of Swords. You could then consider the relationship between these cards in conjunction with the relevant planetary interpretations.

Date:

Your personal significator card:

The card you would most like to aspire to:

Your alter-ego card:

Your family cards:
Father:

Mother:

Brother:

Sister:

Other family members who are especially significant to you:

Predominant element in your family:

Element least present:

Sun sign card:
Moon sign card (if known):
Ascendant card (if known):

EXERCISES FOR THE MINOR ARCANA

Whether the Major and Minor Arcana were actually conceived of together or separately is not known: the answer is shrouded in the mystery of the Tarot's origin. All we can do today is look at the way they work together in harmony. While the Major Arcana signify the larger archetypal forces at work in each human being's life, the Minor illustrate the more specifically individual aspects of those archetypes. The Court cards act as a bridge between the two by describing various archetypal personality types. By now you will have become aware of the Court cards and astrological personalities, with which you are most closely identified.

The Minor Arcana flesh out the broad patterns which influence everyone's life at some time or another. They expand the psychological description as indicated by the Major Arcana, and give clues to possible coming events. To make each suit more vivid and dramatic, a myth has been selected which reflects the suit's individual character and runs through from Ace to Ten. Although strictly speaking the myths do not have any connection with the Tarot, they do aid in understanding the cards and thus make them easier to remember in the course of readings. More importantly, however, each suit and myth develops a theme around a particular sphere of human experience. As we have seen, the suit of Cups relates to feelings, Wands to creativity, Swords to the intellect and Pentacles to the material world. Each myth tells a story relating to each of these four realms of experience. Although the myths may sometimes appear inapplicable to modern life on the surface, their underlying themes are profoundly relevant. Psychologically, mankind has not altered so very much in the course of the centuries. People still fall in love, as did Eros and Psyche in the myth which unfolds through the suit of Cups. People still embark on adventurous enterprises, as did Jason and the Argonauts in the myth describing the suit of Wands. Families still have horrendous battles, the evils of which are still visited upon the children, as illustrated in the myth of Orestes, connected with the suit of Swords. People still need to establish material security and create solid lasting forms, as did Daedalus, the master craftsman, whose myth relates to the suit of Pentacles. Although we might like to think we have changed a lot over the centuries, we may well be surprised to discover how closely these myths parallel our daily lives and experience.

In order to acquire a more meaningful picture of the Minor Arcana, it will help enormously to do some exercises on them yourself. You might, for example, picture yourself as the hero or heroine of each suit. Can you imagine yourself as heroic Jason, anguished Orestes, lovelorn Psyche or wily Daedalus? Try to imagine yourself as part of each story. How would you feel in each situation? Do the mythological adventures reflect the more mundane patterns in your own life? Another exercise might be to write your own myth, using the suits, their numbers and divinatory meanings as your outline. It would be a formidable challenge to your creativity and an opportunity to test, flex and expand your imagination. Such exercises are intended to stimulate the imagination and stir up the unconscious archetypal patterns within. At the same time they will also foster greater familiarity with the cards. Although the traditional divinatory meanings remain unchanged in *The Mythic Tarot*, the methods for developing greater understanding through your own resources have been augmented. For instance, the Three of Cups depicts 'celebration, rejoicing, a happy event'. But understanding the background to the celebration helps to give a fuller and richer interpretation when reading the cards.

The Minor Arcana can bring us closer to the everyday situations that each suit reflects. You are therefore encouraged to imagine a situation of your own which you can identify with each card. Thus the meaning will become personalised and the card more familiar. Space is reserved in the Workbook for you to record your personal impressions which will become an invaluable reference in your study of Tarot. The effort is well worth making if you are to become a competent and experienced Tarot reader.

[handwritten: feelings / cups]

ACE OF CUPS

[handwritten: +]

Mythological reference: *Aphrodite*

Divinatory meaning: Upsurge of feelings and emotion, new relationships.

The Cups are the suit connected with the realm of feeling. The Ace, being the number one, contains a highly potent emotional energy. This energy might lead to a new relationship or the revival of an old one. The intensity of feelings is often felt by others, and new friendships or partnerships can thus be attracted. A love affair may begin, or the birth of a child may foster immense love and tenderness. Aphrodite, the goddess of love and relationships, harmonious or otherwise, presides over this card and the whole suit of Cups. When the Ace of Cups appears, you may be sure that the capricious goddess will not be far away. Aphrodite launches the tale of Eros and Psyche, a famous love story which contains many elements of today's popular

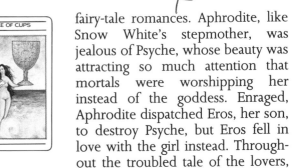

ACE OF CUPS

fairy-tale romances. Aphrodite, like Snow White's stepmother, was jealous of Psyche, whose beauty was attracting so much attention that mortals were worshipping her instead of the goddess. Enraged, Aphrodite dispatched Eros, her son, to destroy Psyche, but Eros fell in love with the girl instead. Throughout the troubled tale of the lovers, Aphrodite played the part of wicked mother-in-law. But although the intention was to destroy Psyche, it was actually the making of her. The difficulties the lovers encountered in being together forced them to the realisation of how important their love was. Without Aphrodite, they would not have met at all. Dwell upon the meaning of this card for you and record your observations.

[handwritten: Start out slow & enthusiasm]

Date: *[handwritten: All beginnings with]*

Recall an experience of your own which fits this image's essence: *[handwritten: feelings]*

Find your own key word or phrase for this card:

TWO OF CUPS

Mythological reference: The meeting of Eros and Psyche.
Divinatory meaning: Commitment to romance, partnership or friendship.

In the Two of Cups, the pure energy of the Ace has polarised. The Two often indicates the early days of a relationship, when the power of love and attraction is great. The first flush of love, which is usually in evidence at the start of any affair, is symbolised by the meeting of Eros and Psyche. The Tarot image portrays their first encounter, with Psyche imprisoned on her lonely rock, awaiting her death, and Eros approaching her. Aphrodite, jealous of Psyche's beauty, instructed her son to kill the girl. Contrary to his mother's wishes, Eros, having pricked himself on one of his golden arrows, fell deeply in love with Psyche on first sight. Instead of killing Psyche, he rescued her. It is not unusual, at the beginning of a love affair,

TWO OF CUPS

to see one's partner without any faults. We are so attracted by the person's positive qualities that his or her failings are often overlooked. The Two of Cups describes the kind of 'blind love' which is so typical of a new relationship. 'It is too good to be true,' say the couple, 'We get on so perfectly. We understand each other completely.' In order to appreciate the glowing energy generated by the Two of Cups, think about a similar situation from your own experience. Think of the time you first fell in love. Were you 'blinded' by your emotions? Try to recapture the excitement, awe and magic that attend such a state of mind. Recall the experience, then write it down with all the feelings and associations evoked, in the space below.

Date:

Recall an experience of your own which fits this image's essence:

Find your own key word or phrase for this card:

THREE OF CUPS

Mythological reference: The marriage of Eros and Psyche.
Divinatory meaning: Celebration, time of rejoicing.

THREE OF CUPS

The Three of Cups indicates an initial completion. The first phase is over. In the case of the Cups, the Three often marks the end of the first stage of falling in love and suggests that commitment to a future has been made. Or it may signify that the initial making of a baby through conception and gestation is completed, permitting the birth to take place. Although there is much work to be done in the future, the Three marks a stage for rejoicing. The image depicts the marriage of Eros and Psyche. Although Eros loved Psyche on sight, there was little recognition of the woman behind the persona. Psyche, for her part, was blind to her husband's identity, only knowing he was her saviour and loving him for that. It is true that many couples do not have much idea who the other partner is until long after the ceremony has taken place. Samuel Rogers said: 'It does not much signify whom one marries, as one is sure to find next morning that it is someone else.' Many fairy tales end with the protagonists living 'happily ever after', and many couples seem to be under the misapprehension that marriage is the end goal, not the first step on a long road. The story of Eros and Psyche goes on to relate the sacrifices, tribulations and betrayals, as well as the love and loyalty, that form the substance of most partnerships. Can you call to mind the celebration of an initial completion? Try to find from your own experience a situation which might echo the sentiments of the Three of Cups.

Date:

Recall an experience of your own which fits this image's essence:

Find your own key word or phrase for this card:

FOUR OF CUPS

Mythological reference: Psyche's jealous sisters breed discontent.
Divinatory meaning: Boredom, depression, discontent and resentment.

The Four of Cups indicates a sense of betrayal and apathy which can prevent a positive seeking of new paths. This sense of anticlimax or depression is quite common when marriage, childbirth or any other event which, after an elaborate ritualised build-up, must be confronted and worked with in its more mundane aspects, on a daily basis.

For Psyche the time after her marriage is initially one of pleasure, her every wish being met for her as if by magic. She lives in a magnificent palace and invisible servants do her every bidding. The major disadvantage is that she does not know who her bridegroom really is. He comes to her in the dark of night and warns her never to try to discover his identity. Her jealous sisters symbolise the

FOUR OF CUPS

voices within her, which keep prodding her to seek the truth. The struggle between wanting to know her husband's identity and being reluctant to jeopardise her contentment causes depression and discontent. Eventually the voices of her sisters make her so uncomfortable that Psyche is forced against her will to determine who Eros really is, monster or angel. The more Psyche's sisters press her to ascertain the truth, the more Eros insists that she must not. Unless she makes a move, Psyche's life will be charming but stagnant. For the sake of her own growth, she must find out. Can you think of any event or situation which conjures up for you a sense of Psyche's dilemma? Try to find a parallel in your own experience.

Date:

Recall an experience of your own which fits this image's essence:

Find your own key word or phrase for this card:

crisis point (handwritten)

FIVE OF CUPS

Mythological reference: Psyche finds out the truth and is abandoned by Eros.
Divinatory meaning: Regret over past actions, loss or betrayal in love or marriage.

The Five of Cups is a card of loss and regret. Four cups have been overturned and all their contents spilled out while one is still standing intact. This indicates that although things have gone wrong, although certain decisions have perhaps been made which resulted in chaos, there is yet something remaining which is complete and can be worked on. There may be separation in a relationship caused by a betrayal of trust, but this does not mean that all is forever lost. Psyche is finally pushed by her inner voices to find out whether her husband is an angel or beast. She lights an oil lamp while he is asleep and so discovers her husband is really a beautiful god. She then truly falls in love with him but in her excitement she drops some scalding oil on his shoulder. This wakes him and he departs in disappointment. Something has been lost, but now she knows who her husband really is Psyche wants him for herself. She must now set about trying to get him back. It is not an uncommon situation in everyday life that one member of a couple is dissatisfied and betrays the relationship. Only when the bond is on the point of dissolution does one appreciate how much it means. Then energy once more flows, enabling one to retrieve, repair and maintain the union. In some ways it is perhaps sad that Psyche had to betray Eros, but it was partly his fault for not being more honest with her. Love cannot truly flourish in an atmosphere of pretence. What ideas and associations are evoked for you?

hardship (handwritten)

Date:

Recall an experience of your own which fits this image's essence:

Find your own key word or phrase for this card:

Decide a course of action [handwritten]

Meditate Contemplate [handwritten]

SIX OF CUPS

Mythological reference: *Psyche remembers the past with nostalgia.*
Divinatory meaning: *Past effort may bring present rewards or an old lover may reappear.*

SIX OF CUPS

The Six of Cups depicts a card of nostalgia and happy memories, some of which may bear fruit in the present. It indicates a sentimental time, quite peaceful and calm, in which past events are reflected upon. The card implies an acceptance of the past and the way events happened, but also a sense that certain things have unwittingly been engendered which can be brought to fruition. There is nostalgia, but also a sense that a long-cherished dream could become a future reality. Psyche is portrayed seated sadly upon her lonely rock, where she had first encountered Eros. Her beautiful palace, her husband and all the trappings of her enchanted life having vanished. She is left with her happy memories, but this is not a time for regret.

She must accept what has happened. And she must either relinquish it or make plans for getting Eros back. The Five of Cups reflects the phase when a love affair or marriage has come to a crisis point. The Six of Cups suggests time is needed for recapitulation and for deciding upon a course of action, whether to pursue the affair or allow it to recede into one's other memories, some happy, some sad. One must take the opportunity to reflect on the past and all that it contains. Something from that past will turn out to be of great value, so it is worth spending time in meditation. Can you remember a time of regret or nostalgia following a relationship going wrong? Make a note below of all your spontaneous associations.

Date:

Recall an experience of your own which fits this image's essence:

harmony balance [handwritten]

Find your own key word or phrase for this card:

must act

SEVEN OF CUPS

Mythological reference: Psyche must beg for assistance from Aphrodite.
Divinatory meaning: There is an exceptional choice to be made with many options open. Careful decisions must be made.

The Seven of Cups augurs a time of much creative potential and a great deal of available energy. Many options are open but can only be substantial through hard effort. Otherwise they will remain forever 'castles in the air'. The Seven implies that it is no good just wishing your life away. At a certain moment the time for action will be upon you and you will have to act. Psyche must confront her jealous mother-in-law, because the hostile goddess is the only one who can help her win back Eros. Aphrodite is not going to make the task easy. She prescribes a series of gruelling and humiliating tasks for Psyche to complete. But Psyche, aided by her own instincts and by the creatures of the wood, manages to pass the tests imposed upon her.

She knows this is the only way to make her dream of love from the Six of Cups come true. She must obey the goddess' dictates and humbly perform everything required of her. Once we can make a true commitment to a dream, goal or aspiration, things hence become much easier. The meditation and contemplation of the Six of Cups pay off. The various options and choices are laid before you. They require careful consideration and then definite action must be taken. See if you can relate any of your own experience to Psyche's. The situations described in the myth are not uncommon in daily life. Linking your personal experience with the archetypal can be an interesting exercise. Fill the space below with your own thoughts and ideas.

Date:

Recall an experience of your own which fits this image's essence:

Find your own key word or phrase for this card:

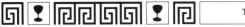 

EIGHT OF CUPS

Mythological reference: Psyche must make the perilous journey to the underworld.
Divinatory meaning: Leaving the past behind, abandoning or relinquishing hope.

Abandon
resignation

The Eight of Cups reflects a situation when the only solution is to let go. No matter how much energy or effort has been put into something, it is still not working, and the only option left is to abandon it. The eight neatly stacked cups symbolise the effort that has been invested in vain. Such a sorry development frequently occurs in relationships: no matter how much one sacrifices or tries to change, the relationship is just not working or appropriate, and the only response is to walk away. This is what Psyche must do when Aphrodite imposes the final test upon her: to make a journey to Hades' kingdom and borrow a pot of beauty cream from Persephone. Psyche knows that this trip means almost certain death, yet she has no option but to risk her life. She has completed all the other tasks demanded of her. She is now commanded to abandon hope, for that is her only hope. This card carries with it a sense of resignation, acceptance and some sadness, but the choice is voluntary. When a relationship becomes lifeless and there is no growth or development, the only answer may be to leave. Psyche has a dim hope that her trip might be successful, but she is fully prepared to die. The abandonment must often be as heartfelt as that for any positive change to occur. One must be prepared never to return to the situation should things not change. If you have experienced that kind of resignation, call it to mind and write down your experience and associations.

Date:

Recall an experience of your own which fits this image's essence:

Find your own key word or phrase for this card:

NINE OF CUPS

Mythological reference: Psyche and Eros are finally reunited with Aphrodite's blessing.
Divinatory meaning: A wish of paramount importance will come true.

The Nine of Cups signifies great emotional joy. A long cherished dream is finally realised, amid great ecstasy and genuine love. It is a card which suggests sensual pleasure and satisfaction. Psyche finally returns from the underworld, rescued from the deathlike sleep which imprisoned her when she attempted to borrow Persephone's cream for Aphrodite. When Eros sees the lengths that Psyche was prepared to go for love of him, his heart softens and he wakes her from her deep sleep. This time he admits his fault in keeping secrets and the couple face each other openly at last. The image depicts the second marriage of Eros and Psyche. This time they stand face to face and with the consent of the great goddess Aphrodite. A marriage made with

NINE OF CUPS

dishonesty and falsehoods cannot be expected to last happily. Only when the worst sides of both partners are revealed and accepted can the marriage really begin to flourish. It is often the marriages that work through the greatest trials which eventually yield the most fruitful relationships. The trials which Eros and Psyche underwent willingly resulted in the opportunity to re-work their relationship, this time more honestly. The Nine of Cups may also signify any wish of great importance or value coming true. The achievement of a dearly held dream or desire is heralded. Perhaps you have experienced the special moment when such a dream has come true. Can you recall the joy of the realisation? Make notes of your feelings.

Date:

Recall an experience of your own which fits this image's essence:

Find your own key word or phrase for this card:

TEN OF CUPS

Mythological reference: Psyche gains immortality and joins Eros on Olympus.
Divinatory meaning: Happiness and contentment, with a sense of permanence and future purpose.

TEN OF CUPS

The Ten of Cups indicates a lasting contentment rather different from the ecstasy of the Nine of Cups, in which the realisation of a wish brought heady intoxication and rapture. The sense of ongoing peace is much gentler and less passionate than the mood signified by the Nine. The Ten suggests a love which grows steadily and embraces others. It often suggests the founding of a family, so that the passion which once united the couple now extends to love of children as well. When love has been firmly established, the harmony will not be seriously disrupted, even though disagreements cause a tremor from time to time. Psyche now achieves immortality and, as a goddess, is permitted to live on Olympus, the dwelling place of the gods. The myth goes on to reveal that Eros and Psyche gave birth to a daughter whose name was Pleasure, reflecting the pleasure they gain from each other as well as from their child. This sense of harmony and contentment is an oft-sought goal, and is not easily achieved. Such satisfaction requires much effort and hard work, but there is nevertheless the encouraging awareness that it can be realised if we are prepared to pay the price. Think about the meaning of this card in context of the whole story and see if there is any parallel in your own experience. Can you see the thread of this myth running through your own life? Make notes of all your feelings and associations, not only in connection with this card but with the whole suit of Cups.

Date:

Recall an experience of your own which fits this image's essence:

Find your own key word or phrase for this card:

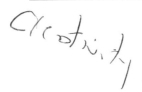 *Creativity*

ACE OF WANDS

+

Mythological reference: Zeus
Divinatory meaning: An upsurge of creative energy, great potential for success.

The Ace of Wands depicts the mighty Zeus bearing a huge flaming wand. The energy which the Ace of Wands image offers is that of creative, imaginative and inspirational vision. It represents the energy which is needed to spark off ideas for any new venture, whether it be of a business or artistic kind. Zeus presides over this card and starts the suit of Wands because it was he who provided the Golden Fleece which inspired Jason's great adventure. The Ace of Wands marks a new cycle of creative activity, inspiring action and struggle for new goals and achievements. For Jason to capture the Golden Fleece was no mean task, and in order to make something extraordinary out of nothing special we need that first spark of inspiration. We need

ACE OF WANDS

something which captures and stimulates our imagination enough to make us risk the consequences. The exciting possibilities that lie ahead must be tempting enough for us to give up notions of security and start a new venture on a hunch. The Ace of Wands indicates the feeling of confidence required to start work on a new venture, be it a book, painting or another form of art or business proposition. It suggests the upsurge of ideas and imagination as well as the drive and energy necessary to undertake such projects. The stimulus which the Ace of Wands represents is the first essential factor that is required. See if you have any feelings from your own experience which can be connected to the essence of this card.

Sleepy, tiring + enthusiasm

Date: *New beginnings in*

Recall an experience of your own which fits this image's essence: *Creativity*

turning

point

Find your own key word or phrase for this card:

TWO OF WANDS

Mythological reference: Chiron has revealed his birthright to Jason.
Divinatory meaning: Courage and initiative available to overcome obstacles.

The two wands placed firmly on the ground indicate that the initial inspiration has found a tentative starting point, a beginning has now been formed. Much courage and perseverance will be necessary to reap the full benefit, but the initial ideas have already become firmly established. The enormous upsurge of energy in the Ace has been challenged in the Two of Wands and a sense pervades this card that the necessary preparation has been made. There is energy and strength to go ahead and attain the goal in question. In many ways, the Two of Wands is a transition card: after the brainwave of the Ace and before the initial completion which is reached in the Three of Wands, there is time during which firm plans must be formu-

lated. Jason is depicted leaving the security of his tutor Chiron's cave. He has found his first goal: to avenge his father, rightful king of Iolkos, imprisoned by his wicked brother Pelias. Jason has been in exile from his home city, under the protection and instruction of Chiron. His education finished, Chiron reveals the truth of his birth and Jason prepares to claim his birthright. Where his journey will take him ultimately is not yet clear, but the first step is ready to be taken. If this card calls to mind any similarities from your own experience, write them down below. Can you recall a time in your life when initial inspiration has prompted action? Have you ever felt like Jason, starting out on a new adventure, uncertain where it will take you?

Date:

Recall an experience of your own which fits this image's essence:

Find your own key word or phrase for this card:

THREE OF WANDS

Mythological reference: Jason confronts King Pelias and is inspired by a quest for the Golden Fleece.
Divinatory meaning: A stage of initial completion of a creative project, with new ideas forming on the horizon.

THREE OF WANDS

The Three of Wands marks the first stage of a project successfully reached. On reaching it, however, new possibilities are revealed which had not previously been apparent. The goal we had originally sought has been attained but we suddenly become aware of larger, more exciting vistas opening before us. One has reached somewhere one thought would be the end, only to discover it is but the very beginning. Jason set off enthusiastically with the goal of regaining the crown of Iolkos. He confronted King Pelias boldly although he was wearing only one sandal, having lost the other in a stream. Pelias had been warned by an oracle to beware of a man wearing one sandal and he handed over the crown without a murmur. Jason thus effectively achieved his objective. But Pelias then subtly suggested that Jason might like to seek the Golden Fleece and thereby bring honour to Iolkos. Jason was instantly inspired by this new challenge. Winning back the crown of Iolkos suddenly pales to insignificance against the luminous prospect of the Golden Fleece. As a result, the potential now made available for the new adventure has overtaken the satisfaction of the successful achievement of the initial goal. There is another period of excitement, with new forces of energy being generated. Have you ever started out to attain a goal and found another as a result? See if you can find correlations in your own life and write them down below.

Date:

Recall an experience of your own which fits this image's essence:

Find your own key word or phrase for this card:

FOUR OF WANDS

Mythological reference: Jason celebrates with his fellow Argonauts as the building of their ship is completed.
Divinatory meaning: A time to pause for celebration after hard efforts.

This card indicates reward after hard labour, like the festival traditionally held when the harvest is brought home. Although only a pause, for much work is yet to follow, it is nevertheless a valid break and marks a pleasant period for deserved rest and relaxation. It could mark a holiday, with time set aside for romance or family enjoyment following the set rigours of daily life.

The Four of Wands image depicts Jason celebrating with his fellow shipmates. They have just completed the painstaking and arduous task of constructing and equipping their ship, the *Argo*, in preparation for the next stage of the adventure. Jason put a great deal of effort not only into construction of the vessel but also in choosing a crew of heroes.

FOUR OF WANDS

He appointed his shipmates for their particular talents: Heracles for his strength, Theseus for his bravery, Orpheus for his talent in music which could soothe troubled minds, and the Warrior Twins for their mercurial intelligence, to name but a few. When at last the job was finished, the occasion was marked with a well-deserved and joyful celebration. In modern everyday life it could perhaps be equated with celebration after exams or the successful completion of a laborious task. Can you think of something special which could conjure up the essence of the Four of Wands? Can you recall the exhilaration following some determined effort? Reflect upon the associations this card calls to mind for you.

Date:

Recall an experience of your own which fits this image's essence:

Find your own key word or phrase for this card:

FIVE OF WANDS

Mythological reference: Jason does battle with the dragon guarding the Golden Fleece.
Divinatory meaning: A time of struggle, petty obstacles constantly appear and cause difficulties.

FIVE OF WANDS

The Five of Wands suggests that life is not smooth but irritating, with annoying details constantly impeding progress. This card marks a phase when the great imaginative and intuitive vision connected with the fiery Wands collides with life's realities. When one is planning a wonderful project the tiniest detail overlooked can grow out of proportion to become a major problem. Jason is seen battling with the dragon and would seem to have underestimated the task. It is only because he has won the heart of Medea, the sorceress, that he triumphs at all, having failed to appreciate the strength of the beast he was confronting.

This kind of struggle often occurs when the grandiose plans of one person meet the stony reality of another's. I recall listening to a man trying to persuade his wife to move to a country with a cold winter climate. When she objected, saying the driveways to the houses were always snowed in and she would be left to shovel the snow, he casually dismissed her protest saying, 'Oh, I'll pay one of the local youngsters to do that.' Needless to say, he was a Fire sign! Jason spent all his energy getting his crew, ship and plans sorted out, without paying too much heed to what he might face in Colchis. Fortunately, he meets with Medea. Thus feminine intuition and wisdom often step in to provide much-needed aid. Have you ever had to face unexpected problems? Write down any associations and feelings this card evokes in you.

Date:

hardship

Recall an experience of your own which fits this image's essence:

Find your own key word or phrase for this card:

SIX OF WANDS

Mythological reference: Jason is triumphant after his successful battle with the dragon.
Divinatory meaning: Public acclaim, promotion, qualification, recognition for work and effort.

The Six of Wands signifies a time of achievement, reward and success, usually in a public sense. It may mean winning a scholarship, gaining a qualification, getting a lead role, publishing a book, achieving a long awaited promotion, or success in any other chosen field. Naturally this does not herald success forevermore. After the peak of achievement comes a new phase of hard work to keep hold of what has been gained. Nevertheless the actual moment of triumph is an exciting one which is worthy of deserved praise and acclaim.

The card shows Jason holding high his trophy of the Golden Fleece. His fellow shipmates cheer him on in his hour of victory. It evokes a heady moment of

SIX OF WANDS

accomplishment, and Jason is experiencing the pure joy of public acclaim. All his plans and dreams have been realised in conquering the formidable enemy of the dragon. This card concentrates on public success, something which can be recognised and appreciated by others. It does not merely signify satisfaction for personal gain. Public recognition of an achievement evokes a feeling quite different from the private, personal sense of satisfaction that flows from a job well done. If you have ever enjoyed popular recognition for your efforts, or even public acclaim, think of how it made you feel. See if you can recall any thoughts and feelings which went with that moment. Write down any other associations this image evokes.

Date:

Recall an experience of your own which fits this image's essence:

harmony
balance

Find your own key word or phrase for this card:

SEVEN OF WANDS

Mythological reference: After the fight with the dragon, more battles ensue.
Divinatory meaning: Stiff competition must now be faced. Renewed determination and courage are necessary.

The Seven of Wands describes the stage after the public recognition or success seen in the Six. Once a high level of achievement has been attained, one is then automatically faced with the next level on and the attendant competition. For example, if you win a race, you are then expected to compete in the next level up, which will be to a higher standard. In effect, the reward for high achievement is a challenge to try even harder. But although we must be on our guard and put more effort into our work, competition can still be stimulating and exciting.

Jason is shown in this image in fierce battle with the armies of Medea's father, King Aeetes. Once again Medea helped Jason and his cause by murdering her brother, whose

limbs she scattered over the oceans. While heartbroken Aeetes stopped to gather the remains of his son and future heir, Jason and his Argonauts made their escape to Iolkos and further victory. Sometimes stiff competition brings out the best in people and sometimes it does not. Jason proved that he could not have succeeded without Medea's help. Sometimes the taste of success does make us act in ways of which we might not be wholly proud. At other times we double our efforts and work extra hard in order to win victory in a worthy fashion. Notice how the Seven follows the Six and determine, from your own experience, how success affects you. Write down the various feelings and associations about the card below.

Date:

Recall an experience of your own which fits this image's essence:

Find your own key word or phrase for this card:

EIGHT OF WANDS

Mythological reference: After the fierce battles are won, the Argonauts are in a smooth stretch and sailing swiftly home.
Divinatory meaning: A period of fruitful progress after a delay or struggle.

The Eight of Wands indicates a time in which delays or setbacks seem to be past and the future looks bright and exciting. This card suggests that the time is ripe for purposeful activity, and that new undertakings will be successful. It marks the wonderful stage in life when everything seems to be on your side. After the difficulties, struggles and delays of the Seven, the Eight of Wands symbolises a time when all proceeds smoothly and according to plan. Although we may think that ideally life should always be like this, we must realise that we need conflict to push us forward. But we also need the reward of peace and encouragement that the Eight of Wands offers, to make the struggle seem justified and worthwhile.

EIGHT OF WANDS

The card image depicts a happy scene, with the *Argo* in full sail proceeding swiftly towards her goal. The sea is calm and the ship is followed by two playful dolphins, the fish of good fortune. This period of fair weather happily follows Jason's narrow escape from Colchis, and, for the moment at least, all is well. We must learn to take full advantage of such productive phases, for the suit of Wands indicates that they do not last forever. The Wands in particular seem to be a suit of peaks and troughs, which is perhaps not a bad description of life in general. Ask whether this card reflects situations in your own life. Recall a time when everything went your way. Describe the feelings and thoughts attending that experience in the space below.

Date:

Recall an experience of your own which fits this image's essence:

Find your own key word or phrase for this card:

NINE OF WANDS

Mythological reference: The final stage of conflict before Jason can reach his ultimate destination.
Divinatory meaning: Strength in reserve can provide enough energy to win the battle, although resources seem exhausted.

NINE OF WANDS

The Nine of Wands implies that there is strength in reserve. This untapped repository often reveals itself when we feel as though we just cannot go on. If we push hard enough, however, we find we can muster enough strength to achieve what seems impossible. In cases of unforseen danger, for instance, it is quite well known that we can find extra resources which normally would not be available. One woman told me of how her small child got trapped beneath a piece of heavy furniture which she would not usually have been able to move. Confronted by the crisis she found a special strength and moved the obstacle to free her child. It is this kind of strength, a strength we do not know we possess until we have to use it, which is portrayed by the image on the Nine of Wands.

The image shows the *Argo* fighting valiantly in stormy seas. Rough weather is depicted, tossing the ship perilously. Extra strength and determination was required to battle through the deadly Clashing Rocks, which claimed many sailors' lives and vessels. But somehow, Jason and his men find enough determination to weather the last stage of the journey. Such reserves of energy can come in useful not only physically, but mentally and emotionally too. When we are at the end of our mental or emotional tethers, the fighting spirit of the Nine of Wands can prove invaluable. If you can think of a personal situation which would relate to this card's energy, write it down in the space below.

Date:

Recall an experience of your own which fits this image's essence:

Find your own key word or phrase for this card:

TEN OF WANDS

Mythological reference: Jason has reached his goal but in striving towards another victory he loses everything.
Divinatory meaning: There is danger implied in taking on more than one can cope with.

The Ten of Wands symbolises burdens which become too oppressive to carry. This card warns of the difficulties which are incurred by not being aware of one's limits. One of the drawbacks of the Fiery element is a faulty sense of limitation or boundary when deciding what to take on and what to turn down. Jason, while full of the positive qualities of Fire, lacks a sense of his own limitations. On returning from Colchis he received great acclaim and was honoured as the King of Ilokos. He lived with Medea and they had several children. After a while, however, Jason became restless and desired another challenge and so he decided to pursue the crown of Corinth. This not unnaturally angered Medea, for in order to

TEN OF WANDS

get the crown Jason married the Princess Creusa. Medea turned her powers of sorcery upon Jason, murdering his new wife and all the children she had borne him. Jason found the burden of two kingdoms excessively restrictive and the prodigious fighting spirit within him simply died. He is pictured oppressed by the Wands of creativity, which were once the breath of life to him. The ending of his myth is an apt illustration of what can happen when we take on more than we can handle, through an inadequate awareness of our limitations. Can you think of an example from your own experience, when you failed to recognise your own limits? Write your associations and thoughts down in the space below.

Date:

Recall an experience of your own which fits this image's essence:

Find your own key word or phrase for this card:

intellect +

ACE OF SWORDS

Mythological reference: Athene
Divinatory meaning: *A card of strength in spite of adversity, an indication that out of apparent evil, good will come.*

The Ace of Swords is a card which suggests inevitable and irrevocable change. As we have seen, all the Aces indicate an upsurge of energy. The Ace of Swords, being connected with the intellect, signifies the awakening of mental powers which may cause conflict at first but are ultimately conducive to growth and development. The Ace of Swords has a double-edged quality. On the one hand, it heralds immense energy; on the other, it is often attended by conflict before a final resolution is achieved. This is illustrated by the story of Orestes, the last in the cursed line of Atreus. The drama of this ill-fortuned house comprises the story for the suit of Swords. The image depicts Athene, goddess of wisdom, brandishing a huge sword. Although Athene does not instigate the story

ACE OF SWORDS

of Orestes, she nevertheless ends it with her just resolution at his trial. As we saw in the card of Justice, the powers of the mind can be used positively to bring justice to mankind; but they can also be negatively manipulative. The quarrels and strife brought to the House of Atreus originated with man's arrogance in the face of the gods. But resolution of the drama also came from the power of the mind, in the form of the first jury over which Athene presided. When the Ace of Swords appears in a reading, you may be sure something is about to change which will have far-reaching consequences for it is a card of great power and force. Think about the energy in this Ace card, and how its essence affects you. Make a note below of all the feelings and thoughts it evokes.

spirit drive + enthusiasm

Date: *new beginnings in intellect*

Recall an experience of your own which fits this image's essence:

Find your own key word or phrase for this card:

TWO OF SWORDS tension suppressed

Mythological reference: Orestes finds himself between his warring parents.
Divinatory meaning: Stalemate; nothing can move or change, a situation of great tension. An impasse has been reached.

The Two of Swords represents a situation in which it appears impossible to move forward. If perfect balance can be maintained, the underlying tension can be momentarily ignored. There is a feeling of unrest, which is very uncomfortable to live with; but the fear of completely upsetting the status quo often makes it preferable to ignore this tension. Such situations are often discernible in one's own relationships, or in other people's. When a couple do not get along well, there is often a deep hostility, yet nobody mentions it. On the contrary, everyone pretends things are fine for fear of facing the fact that a rupture might have to occur. Eventually, of course, the storm must break, for it is almost impossible to maintain the balance forever. The Two of Swords

TWO OF SWORDS

depicts Orestes caught between his father and his mother, who face each other in anger with swords crossed. King Agamemnon, Orestes' father, had sacrificed their daughter for a glorious victory, deceiving his wife, Clytemnestra, by telling her the girl was to be married. When Clytemnestra discovered the truth, she was enraged and resolved to exact revenge on her murdering husband. The tension mounts between them, but Orestes closes his eyes and ears to the situation, not wishing to confront the unpleasantness around him. If you can identify this situation in your own life, write down your experience of it. How long can you bear to live with tension, or are you more afraid of change? In what way does the message of this card affect you?

Date:

Recall an experience of your own which fits this image's essence:

Find your own key word or phrase for this card:

THREE OF SWORDS

Mythological reference: Clytemnestra and her lover murder King Agamemnon.
Divinatory meaning: Quarrels and conflict, a period of stormy weather for relationships. Also relief that tension has been released.

The Three of Swords signifies a time of sorrow, but there is comfort in the recognition that things have to be that way. Even if the situation could have turned out differently, there is a feeling that one would not change it, for it is held necessary, regrettable though it may be. Sometimes we have to let go of something we do not wish to let go of, because we can actually see and understand that this is the best thing to do, perhaps the only thing. A relationship which is not growing and is causing unhappiness must be allowed to die, whatever the short-term pain. The sense of vision and understanding that the Three of Swords brings makes the pain easier to bear. The image depicts the murder scene in which Clytemnestra and her lover

THREE OF SWORDS

murder Agamemnon in his bath. The unhappy chain has passed down through generations, for Agamemnon's heartless murder of his daughter now results in his own death. As revealed in the tension of the Two, each party tries to deceive the other, and Clytemnestra bides her time; now she cannot bear the tension any longer and avenges her daughter's murder. Although the usual interpretation for the Three of Swords is not as melodramatic as in this tale, the card still implies that something sad or painful must be allowed to work itself out. You may have had an experience of something similar. If so, make a note of it below. See how the Three follows on from the Two and try to trace a parallel continuity in your own life.

Initial step complete
hard effort to follow
growth/expansion

Date:

Recall an experience of your own which fits this image's essence:

Find your own key word or phrase for this card:

FOUR OF SWORDS

Mythological reference: Orestes in exile.

Divinatory meaning: A need for rest or retreat after stress, a time for convalescence after physical or emotional tension.

FOUR OF SWORDS

The Four of Swords is a card which signifies calm after the storm. There is a need for time to heal and for energy to be regenerated. After illness, the body needs time to gain strength; and after emotional upset, the feelings need peace and quiet to regain their equilibrium. In the wake of disruption, whether it be separation, divorce, quarrels or anything else, we all need a period of introspection during which we can sift through the events and put them into perspective. If we are wise, we allow and allot such space for putting our inner house in order before entering into the fray again. The Four of Swords depicts Orestes in quiet contemplation as he waits in exile. He was sent away by his mother so that he might not interfere with her plans to murder Agamemnon, and is thus in peace. During this period of inactivity, he is in fact gaining strength for the battles that lie ahead. In our busy modern age, we seem to allow ourselves much less leisure for convalescence and recovery than we used to. We seem to consider it a weakness to relax and recuperate.

We do not even allow much time for mourning after divorce or death, but continue to push ourselves beyond our limits. The Four of Swords is a useful image to dwell upon while you consider how much time you allow yourself for recovery after strain. Do you tend to suppress your personal feelings and get on with life? Or are you in tune with your body's emotional needs? Write your observations down below.

Date:

Recall an experience of your own which fits this image's essence:

Find your own key word or phrase for this card:

FIVE OF SWORDS

Mythological reference: Apollo reveals the truth about Agamemnon's murder.
Divinatory meaning: Pride must be swallowed, and limitations accepted, before further progress can be made.

FIVE OF SWORDS

The Five of Swords signifies the boundaries and limitations we must all accept in certain of life's circumstances. There are times when no amount of will-power or fighting can change a situation; the only way to deal with it is to accept it. The Five of Swords depicts Apollo sternly informing Orestes of his task: to avenge his father's murder. Apollo is a patriarchal god and demands the vengeance of a life for a father's life. This puts Orestes in an agonising position, because he is now being called upon to commit matricide. This will therefore evoke the wrath of the Furies, who deem that a mother's life is of more value than a father's. Nevertheless, and no matter how 'unfair' it seems, Orestes must accept this situation which he cannot alter.

Through no fault of his own, Orestes is placed in an impossible predicament. His parents' sins have fallen squarely upon his shoulders and it is now up to him to assume responsibility for his bloodline. The messy problems of his parents' wrongdoings are passed on to him because he is their son, just or unjust though this may be. At some point during our lives we must assume responsibility for our heritage, whether we like it or not. The Five of Swords reflects a situation in which we are powerless to do anything but accept and work within the framework of that situation. Trying to change it would be as useful as beating your head against a brick wall. Can you find an echo of its meaning in your own experience?

hardship

Date:

Recall an experience of your own which fits this image's essence:

Find your own key word or phrase for this card:

SIX OF SWORDS

Handwritten annotation: A calm after tension, of a big decision

Mythological reference: Orestes sets sail for Argos, where he will carry out the will of Apollo.
Divinatory meaning: A period of calm after great anxiety, release of tension, a peaceful journey towards smoother waters.

The Six of Swords is a card of harmony and denotes the slackening of tension. After a time of great disruption or unhappiness, the Six marks a smooth passage. Sometimes this can mean a physical move away from unpleasant surroundings. But it can also symbolise an inner journey away from anxiety towards peace. The Six depicts Orestes standing with his head held high and his arms folded in resignation; he is prepared to accept his fate and do what is required of him. The waters behind him are rough, but his boat is pointing towards calmer seas. Orestes has come to the decision that he has no other course of action but to avenge his father, dire though the consequences may be. Once a difficult decision has finally been made, there

SIX OF SWORDS

is an immediate sense of relief, even if, as in Orestes' case, the choices are not especially inviting. The agony of indecision before a choice is made is often the worst moment. Once there is a plan, no matter how disagreeable the end result may prove to be, there is a feeling of relief. The Six of Swords does not necessarily imply a doomed choice in a reading. Very often it can signify a change for the better, but usually after a difficult choice has been made. See whether this card can speak to you on any level, and write down whatever feelings and impressions come to mind. Try to feel the calm after the tension of an agonising decision that this card reflects, perhaps imagining yourself in a similar situation and noting the feelings evoked.

Handwritten: harmony balance

Date:

Recall an experience of your own which fits this image's essence:

Find your own key word or phrase for this card:

SEVEN OF SWORDS

Mythological reference: Orestes returns at night to his mother's palace to murder her.
Divinatory meaning: A need for evasion and avoidance of direct confrontation in order to reach an objective.

The Seven of Swords suggests that indirect action, confusing roundabout courses and extreme caution are called for if the objective of the moment is to be attained. It is sometimes necessary to employ evasive tactics and use brain, tact or diplomacy, rather than brawn or aggression, in order to achieve particular goals. We may not like to use such methods, preferring to be more straightforward and honest, but there are times when success demands an oblique approach. The Seven of Swords indicates that dealings cannot be totally direct, and may even be morally or ethically questionable. Orestes is pictured creeping into his old home at the dead of night to carry out the dictates of Apollo. It is obvious that he cannot

SEVEN OF SWORDS

arrive with a fanfare blazoning, when his intention is to murder his mother. He must plan and move discreetly, without attracting attention. Although the Seven of Swords in a reading does not symbolise such melodramatic circumstances as trying to commit murder without getting caught, it does imply that we may be obliged to act in ways that are not totally direct, but which we need to accept, hoping the end will justify the means. Can you recall a situation in which you were required to act in this particular fashion, even though it may have been against your preferred style? What sort of tactics did you employ and were you successful? If you can identify with such an experience, write it down below.

Date:

Recall an experience of your own which fits this image's essence:

Find your own key word or phrase for this card:

EIGHT OF SWORDS

Mythological reference: The full implications of his dilemma dawn on Orestes.
Divinatory meaning: A fear of moving out of a situation of bondage, paralysis, a 'no win' position.

no win position [handwritten annotation]

The Eight of Swords indicates a situation of tension similar to that of the Two. Whereas in the Two they were being suppressed, in this case, however, the choices are now perfectly conscious. The card conveys a sense of being trapped, bound in a situation which causes unhappiness; but the fear of what might happen if one tries to extricate oneself is equally inhibiting. Sometimes material security traps us in a situation with which we are not happy emotionally, but the thought of relinquishing such security is as frightening as being emotionally starved. Orestes is faced with a particularly nasty choice: he faces the wrath of Apollo if he does not commit matricide, and the prospect of madness inflicted by the Furies if he does.

EIGHT OF SWORDS

He is quite literally 'damned if he does and damned if he doesn't'. He must face this decision alone. There is no one else able to shoulder the responsibility for him. He needs to find his own solution and incur the consequences. Ultimately Orestes knows what he must do, for he is a man and must therefore stand up for his father. He must accept the consequences of his birthright. Think of a situation in which you had to face being trapped between equally distasteful alternatives. How did you resolve the situation? How long did it take? What were the feelings like which attended your predicament? How did you make the final choice? Write down your experience and the associated thoughts and emotions.

Date:

Recall an experience of your own which fits this image's essence:

Find your own key word or phrase for this card:

NINE OF SWORDS

Guilt

Mythological reference: Orestes is driven mad by the Furies.
Divinatory meaning: A time in which the mind is tormented by fears of impending doom.

The Nine of Swords suggests that nightmares or fantasies trouble the mind, even though the facts do not match the fears. But though the fears may be ungrounded, they can nevertheless prevent us from ever enjoying ourselves. Sometimes the fears derive from deep-rooted guilt, perhaps about past actions. Guilt is one of the most crippling emotions and it is often difficult to trace its origins. The Nine of Swords depicts Orestes unable to find peace from the menacing Furies. He committed what to the Furies is the worst possible crime, that of matricide, and they torment him in the form of agonising guilt. The Furies cannot inflict physical harm on Orestes, but they persecute him mentally. He is constantly afflicted with terrifying nightmares which,

NINE OF SWORDS

though not real, leave him no peace. Guilt can be the most crippling emotion, and its roots are often buried deep in the past. Sometimes the true guilt is not even our own. Orestes, for example, assumed the guilt of his parents' quarrel as though it were his own, suffering wretchedly as a result. He cannot perceive the surrounding circumstances, seeing only his own destructive actions. When we can understand the reasons for our guilt or fear, the resulting insight can be helpful in dispelling it. What does guilt mean to you? Have you any personal experience which you could use to understand the Nine of Swords better? Write down any such experience, together with your feelings and associations about the card.

Date:

Recall an experience of your own which fits this image's essence:

Find your own key word or phrase for this card:

TEN OF SWORDS

Mythological reference: Athene calls a halt to Orestes' suffering.
Divinatory meaning: The end of a painful situation or state. There emerges an ability to see a situation realistically.

The Ten of Swords marks the resolution of a painful situation. Once something has truly ended, the way is cleared for a fresh start. No matter how traumatic or distressing the ending may be, once it is over the path is open for new growth. Sometimes such an ending comes through seeing a situation clearly, without illusion. Sometimes relationships or partnerships end when we can see our partner as he or she really is, not as we might like him or her to be. The dawning of clear perception can make the ending less painful than it otherwise might be. The Ten of Swords depicts Athene holding back the Furies while Orestes lies, nearly dead with exhaustion, at her feet. Athene, taking pity on Orestes, set up one of the first human juries

TEN OF SWORDS

to judge his case. The vote was split exactly, but Athene cast her vote in favour of Orestes, thus freeing him and his line from the fearsome curse of the Furies. Orestes was allowed to go in peace while Athene appeased the Furies, who were already planning further retribution, by offering them honourable worship in their own shrines.

The Ten of Swords reflects the necessity for a clear break, yet taking all possibilities into consideration. To ignore the Furies would be to leave the way open for further destruction. Think of occasions in your own life when making a clear decisive break that leaves no loose ends, has been necessary. Think of any experience you have had of both: making definite or indefinite breaks.

Date:

Recall an experience of your own which fits this image's essence:

Find your own key word or phrase for this card:

material +

ACE OF PENTACLES

Mythological reference: Poseidon
Divinatory meaning: Material achievement is possible, financial aid may be available for the beginning of a new enterprise.

ACE OF PENTACLES

The Ace of Pentacles represents an upsurge of energy which is directed towards material gain. The Ace is, as always, connected with great drive and enthusiasm, in this instance to create material things. The visions of the Ace of Wands may be translated into actuality with the Ace of Pentacles. As a fertility god, Poseidon represents the raw force of nature in all its power. He thus presides over the suit connected with material ventures. The Ace of Pentacles stands for the special energy required to achieve financial security or status, and thus augurs well for founding new businesses, or enterprises which bring with them monetary reward. Sometimes finances become available just at the right time, enabling one to initiate a new scheme.

Sometimes finances fall into one's lap, assisting the continuation of a worthwhile endeavour. An example of this appeared in the reading for a student who was desperately short of money and trying to complete a training which meant a great deal to her. An unexpected bill had just arrived for £90.00. The Ace of Pentacles turned up in her Tarot reading and two days later she was asked to type a manuscript for which the fee was £90.00! The Ace of Pentacles implies the right energy and external circumstances coming together to create fertile ground for a venture. Think of any experience you have had which might match this card's meaning. Add any feelings, thoughts or impressions which the image evokes in you.

Slept with enthusiasm
new beginnings
in
materialism

Date:

Recall an experience of your own which fits this image's essence:

Find your own key word or phrase for this card:

TWO OF PENTACLES

Mythological reference: Daedalus, the master craftsman, embarks on a new career.
Divinatory meaning: Change and fluctuation in financial matters, but harmony within the change.

TWO OF PENTACLES

The Two of Pentacles reveals a split in the pure energy of the Ace. There is a necessity to be flexible, and to demonstrate the ability to move in several different directions at once. There may be a need to juggle various things in order to keep everything moving, or, in financial terms to 'borrow from Peter to pay back Paul'. The card suggests an optimism and enthusiasm which balances out anxieties about financial affairs. Daedalus, the famous Athenian craftsman, is shown starting out in his trade. Daedalus was renowned for his talent in very intricate metalwork, having been instructed by Athene herself. Although he is best known for his construction of the labyrinth for Minos of Crete, he spent the first half of his life perfecting his art, diversifying and learning new skills. During the early stages of a business, much flexibility and movement is required before it can settle into a pattern. One must be prepared to try different approaches and change a particular method if it is not working efficiently. This requires adaptability, as well as some patience, for the beginning of a venture must not be approached too rigidly. Risks must be incurred while full advantage is taken of all opportunities as they arise. It is an exciting time during which creative use must be made of all material resources at your disposal. If this image conjures up any recollections, write them down. Add any other feelings, associations or ideas you may have.

Date:

Recall an experience of your own which fits this image's essence:

Find your own key word or phrase for this card:

THREE OF PENTACLES

Mythological reference: Daedalus receives acclaim for his first achievements.
Divinatory meaning: Initial completion of work, a basic structure is built which still requires the finishing touches.

The Three of Pentacles is a card which, like all the Threes, signifies an initial stage completed. This first stage must be reached before any further development can take place. It therefore represents a satisfactory time, for there is proof that the project is workable and more detailed work can soon commence. In building a house, for instance, the first bricks-and-mortar stage may not seem terribly exciting, but it is obviously essential before the more enjoyable task of decorating and furnishing can begin. The Three of Pentacles depicts Daedalus receiving rewards for his first works. He has established himself as a talented craftsman and gained admiration for his achievements. At last he has reached a secure platform from which to continue and

THREE OF PENTACLES

perfect his art. He receives recognition from the public, and his work is admired and acknowledged as good. There is cause for celebration, but, as is the case in all the Threes, much hard effort is to follow. This is a card not of final resolution but of secure positive beginnings. Perhaps you can identify the feeling of satisfaction and pride that is reflected in this card. Can you recall an experience of initial good beginnings, whether in your personal or your working life? This card might appear in readings of those who have just bought a house but have not yet moved in, or those who have passed exams but not yet progressed towards a career. Write down your impressions, together with all the associations the card evokes.

Date:

Recall an experience of your own which fits this image's essence:

growth / expansion

Initial stage complete

Find your own key word or phrase for this card:

FOUR OF PENTACLES

Mythological reference: Daedalus realises that his nephew, Talos, is more talented than he.
Divinatory meaning: There is danger in clinging too tightly to what one has earned. Nothing is lost, but nothing can be gained either.

The Four of Pentacles signifies a miserly tendency and reveals the negative attitude inherent in holding on to what one has at the expense of embracing anything new and fresh. Miserliness, usually associated with money, can be extended to the realm of feelings. Freud pointed out the connection between money and emotions: one's attitude towards money as a valuable commodity can be linked to one's feelings about oneself and others as valuable and worthwhile. Thus, meanness with money is associated with lack of emotional generosity. There may be as much fear of losing emotionally as there is of losing financially. Another emotion comes in here, that of envy. The Four of Pentacles depicts Daedalus glaring furiously at his

FOUR OF PENTACLES

talented nephew and clutching tightly to his four pentacles. Not only does he want to keep the money and fame to himself in a miserly fashion, he cannot bear the envy he feels when he sees his nephew progressing and becoming more skilled than himself. Daedalus is not spurred on by a sense of challenge or competition. On the contrary, he stagnates and refuses to do anything. The envy Daedalus feels only spoils what talents he has, and he does not use it as an incentive to improve his own standards. How would you react in his situation? Would the competition spur you on, or cause you to stop trying? Write down your associations with this card including as much as possible from your own experience.

Date:
Recall an experience of your own which fits this image's essence:

Find your own key word or phrase for this card:

FIVE OF PENTACLES

Mythological reference: Daedalus flees Athens, leaving behind all he has worked for.
Divinatory meaning: Loss of financial hardship. Loss on a deeper level; of esteem, of faith in oneself and in life.

The Five of Pentacles warns of the danger of loss. There may be loss on a financial level also, perhaps following from the stagnating sense of the Four. It may be that while struggling to keep hold of what one has, one actually risks losing everything, which is the result in the Five. There is another warning about losing faith in oneself and in life, and this is often even greater than a financial loss. The Five of Pentacles depicts Daedalus furtively hurrying away from his workshop, leaving behind all his hard-earned pentacles, symbol of his success. Daedalus' envy of Talos finally became so unbearable that he threw the youth off the roof of the workshop. The murder was discovered and Daedalus was obliged to flee in haste, leaving behind

FIVE OF PENTACLES

everything he had achieved. This card suggests financial loss or emotional hardship, but there is also an implication that the loss has been brought about by one's own hand. Daedalus lost everything because of his inability to cope with his envy and the sense of inadequacy his nephew's talent evoked in him. In other words, he brought the hardship and downfall upon himself. This may not be a comforting thought, but it does provide a basis for starting again, bearing in mind one's shortcomings. One will therefore be better equipped to tackle the problem differently next time. This card may reflect a stage to which you can relate personally. If so, write down your own experience and associations below.

hardship

Date:

Recall an experience of your own which fits this image's essence:

Find your own key word or phrase for this card:

SIX OF PENTACLES

Mythological reference: Daedalus finds a benevolent friend in King Minos of Crete.
Divinatory meaning: Help from a generous friend or employer, a situation in which there is money or good fortune to be shared.

The Six of Pentacles signifies that assistance comes when it is most needed, partly through fortunate circumstances and partly through one's own efforts. It can manifest itself as a sudden windfall or finances becoming available at just the appropriate time. There is a resulting mood of well-being and security, with faith in life and one's own self-esteem regained. After the traumas pictured in the Five of Pentacles, the Six offers an opportunity to restore equilibrium and faith through the kindness of others. It is a card which suggests charity or support from a benevolent friend, or an opportunity for material rewards to be shared with others.

A new cycle of fortune begins for Daedalus, with King Minos' offering of court patronage.

SIX OF PENTACLES

His crime has been paid for in terms of his own suffering and humiliation, and now he is offered another chance with a generous benefactor. The Sixes are all connected with a sense of harmony and balance, and the Six of Pentacles is no exception. Following the hardships that all the Fives share, there is a respite and an opportunity to regain some of the losses in the Six. Can you think of an occasion when you were in great need of financial or emotional assistance and found it through the kindness and generosity of a friend or employer? Or perhaps the plight of a friend evoked in you a similar generosity of spirit? Call to mind any experiences of sharing and generosity and write them down, together with any other associations.

Date:

Recall an experience of your own which fits this image's essence:

Find your own key word or phrase for this card:

SEVEN OF PENTACLES

Mythological reference: Daedalus is confronted with a new dilemma in the form of a request from Queen Pasiphae.
Divinatory meaning: A difficult decision must be made, between material security and uncertain new opportunities.

The Seven of Pentacles represents a possible change in direction. A certain degree of material security has been established and it would be possible to settle back and be content with what one has achieved. At the same time, however, another idea or inspiration is emerging. One must decide whether to adhere to the tried and tested or embark on a new course which may be risky. We can fall back on material security and the comfort of knowing where we stand, or we can gamble everything on a dream or fantasy which promises to fulfil deep creative desires. The Seven of Pentacles depicts Daedalus well established in Minos' court, six pentacles mounted upon the column signifying the fruit of his labours. Pasiphae, Minos' wife, has incurred an insane passion for her husband's

SEVEN OF PENTACLES

finest bull. The god Poseidon inflicted this passion upon her to punish Minos, who tried to deceive him. Pasiphae implores Daedalus to aid her by constructing a wooden cow for her so that, having crawled into it, she might then mate with the bull. This naturally puts Daedalus in a difficult position. To help Pasiphae would be to betray his master, but to deny her would be to deny the god Poseidon. She is offering only a single pentacle, but as her request reflects the will of the gods, Daedalus decides to help her. The union results in the birth of the Minotaur and Daedalus is requested to build the famous labyrinth. What would you do, faced with a choice between material security and creative inspiration? Write down the associations and experiences this card evokes in you.

Date:

Recall an experience of your own which fits this image's essence:

Find your own key word or phrase for this card:

EIGHT OF PENTACLES

Mythological reference: Daedalus is obliged to start over once again, this time in Sicily.
Divinatory meaning: The apprentice, training or starting out anew in another profession.

EIGHT OF PENTACLES

The Eight of Pentacles is the card of the 'second-time-around apprentice', or the mature student. It often denotes a person who has perhaps worked in a particular field for some years but decides to change direction completely, making a new start from the beginning. It is not the card of the apprentice college-leaver, but more of the mature person starting again, with much experience of life on which to draw. The card suggests the energy, enthusiasm for hard work, and the thirst for knowledge which are often much more evident in mature students than in those fresh from school. The Eight of Pentacles reveals Daedalus, having made his choice in favour of Pasiphae, starting over yet again at the court of King Cocalus of Sicily. King Cocalus did not appear to mind Daedalus' chequered record, for he happily provided the craftsman with plenty of work. Not surprisingly, he incurred the wrath of Minos, who imprisoned Daedalus in the labyrinth he had constructed himself. Daedalus with his ingenuity constructed a pair of wings, and, aided by Pasiphae, escaped from Crete, flying like a bird until he reached Sicily. Undaunted by his past experience, Daedalus begins his career again in the court of Cocalus. Have you ever found yourself in a position of wanting to change direction? Have you started a new training or new way of life at a time when most people think you should be stable and settled? If so, write down your experiences and the various thoughts and feelings which attended the event.

Date:

Recall an experience of your own which fits this image's essence:

Find your own key word or phrase for this card:

NINE OF PENTACLES

Mythological reference: Daedalus is at last able to enjoy the fruits of his labours.
Divinatory meaning: A card of great satisfaction and pleasure, reward for effort, and material benefits.

The Nine of Pentacles implies the satisfaction which stems from personal achievement. It implies the state of physical and emotional well-being which is fostered by an awareness of one's own achievements. The Nine also suggests a solitude which does not mean a lack of relationship but, rather, an ability to rely on oneself; one does not need the constant support of others. The Nine of Pentacles depicts Daedalus wearing rich robes and standing with an air of contentment in a luxuriant garden. He appears self-satisfied and pleased with his lot, for he is in the fortunate position of being able to enjoy what he has worked so long and hard to achieve. He has escaped the final danger of Minos, who tracked him down to Sicily, and found security and appreciation at the court

NINE OF PENTACLES

of Cocalus. His craftsmanship was so cherished by Cocalus, and his daughters so admired the beautiful things Daedalus made them, that they poured boiling water into Minos' bath, thus speedily disposing of him. Daedalus can at last feel secure and at peace. Although his past has been chequered with triumphs and failures, he has come through to a point which enables him to safely enjoy the fruits of his life's labour. This is a unique card. No other image in the Tarot signifies the degree of permanence and the sense of self-esteem that this one does. If you have ever been able to feel confident and comfortable enough to relax in your own accomplishment, try to recapture the mood of that time and record your feelings of that experience in the space provided below.

Date:

Recall an experience of your own which fits this image's essence:

Find your own key word or phrase for this card:

TEN OF PENTACLES

Mythological reference: Daedalus as an old man is able to put down firm roots and found his dynasty.
Divinatory meaning: Financial stability and foundation for home and family.

The Ten of Pentacles signifies a time of real comfort and material abundance. There is contentment in the achievement of something solid and permanent which can be handed down through future generations. There is a special sense of satisfaction in constructing something which will survive long into the future. This might assume the form of children who will continue the family name and tradition, or in the form of creative 'children' such as books, paintings, sculpture or other works of art. The Ten of Pentacles is suggestive of the family blessing which can be passed through the generations. It stands in contrast to the family curse, which we saw expressed through the Swords in the haunted line of Atreus. The Ten of Pentacles image depicts Daedalus, now old and grey,

TEN OF PENTACLES

with his children and grandchildren grouped happily around him. They appear to be enjoying the products of the old man's skill in the form of a necklace, a toy horse and a golden rattle. During his old age, Daedalus can take comfort from the fact that his craft will survive even when he is gone, and that what he fought so hard to maintain will not be lost to future generations. This card often has a connection with buying property, which can be seen as a step to founding a future. The bricks and mortar which constitute a building can remain through the ages; a container for the vital spirits which fill it with life. Consider what in your own life you have created or constructed that could be passed on. See how the essence of this card affects you and write down your associations to it below.

Date:

Recall an experience of your own which fits this image's essence:

Find your own key word or phrase for this card:

General Exercises

Take the forty Minor Arcana cards and spread them out before you. Contemplate the whole deck at length.

Which cards stand out? Which cards or suits are you particularly drawn to? Which cards or suits do you find less appealing? Select the cards you feel most comfortable with and lay them to one side. Now choose the ones you feel least at ease with and set them aside. Give thought to the reasons for your ease or discomfort that each set of cards evoke. Make notes about them in the space provided. Try to discover the key point of appeal or dislike.

Look at the set of forty cards as a whole once again and choose the cards which most echo your life's experiences. Which are those most familiar and most often encountered in your life? Now choose those you would like to encounter more often but perhaps have not had the opportunity.

Group the cards into sets of numbers: Aces, Twos, Threes, and so on. Look at each set of numbers in turn, noticing how each number has its own resonance. Notice how each number is expressed differently through each suit and its element. See how the Aces have tremendous energy in common: they all indicate new beginnings of a vital positive nature, but the energy of the card is chan-

nelled through the element of each different suit. Thus the Ace of Cups expresses new beginnings in the realm of feelings while the Ace of Wands expresses new beginnings in the realm of creativity, and so on. Look at the Twos, revealing the opposites which need to be balanced. The Threes suggest the initial completion, a number of growth and expansion. The Fours are fixed, revealing a sense of energy that is stuck. The Fives represent uncertainty, shifting and changing, and display a mood of adversity in all the suits. The Sixes suggest equilibrium and harmony restored. They present a positive image in all the suits. The Sevens dispel the harmony of the Sixes and fresh dilemmas of choice are presented in all the suits. The Eights stand for regeneration and new ways forward, while the Nines form a base for completion of the cycle in the Tens. Contemplate the groups of numbers at length. Find your own key phrase or word for each set of numbers, for example, Aces: new beginnings, Fives: fluctuation, Tens: permanence. Find the number with which you identify most deeply. For instance, do you feel you are always beginning but never ending; do you relate more easily to the Ace than the Ten? Can you see the numbers as representing a stage in a journey? It is useful to develop a 'feel' for each number so that its influence can be easily understood within a reading, and individually.

Date:

Cards you chose which you felt drawn to:

Cards you chose which you found appealing:

Cards you chose which you felt comfortable with:

Key point of appeal:

Note preference of number or suit, if any:

Cards you chose which you felt repulsed by:

Cards you chose which did not appeal to you:

Cards you chose which you felt uncomfortable with:

Key point of dislike:

Note preference of number or suit, if any:

Make notes on the sets of numbers. Find a key word or phrase for each set.

Aces

Twos:

Threes:

Fours:

Fives:

Sixes:

Sevens:

Eights:

Nines:

Tens:

READING THE CARDS

Before we start to examine readings in detail it may be useful to re-examine what the Tarot cards can and cannot do. They can, and do, provide opportunities to view the situation facing you or the seeker, with some clarity, thus giving structure with which to consider the matter further, perhaps in a different light. They cannot and do not predict a fixed or fated future. Our future is shaped as we live each day. The future can certainly be affected by the past, and the choices we make in the present will obviously have bearing on the future. But the choice is our own, not something pre-ordained and thus immovable. The cards can suggest certain tendencies and influences (often unconscious), which are present in one's life, for the cards act as mirrors, reflecting knowledge from the unconscious mind and making it known to the conscious. Thus the cards can reveal courses of action which might be followed, given the circumstances.

Reading the Tarot for Oneself

There are those who maintain that reading Tarot for oneself is 'unlucky' or in some way invalid. I do not believe this to be true. In fact, readings for oneself can be most valuable, but there are pitfalls. When considering a layout for oneself there is an obvious lack of objectivity. Your particular problem or dilemma cannot receive the benefit of another person's interpretation, but nonetheless, if approached correctly, the cards themselves can provide the 'other point of view'. It rather depends upon whether you are able to suspend your own judgement of your situa-

tion and allow yourself to view the cards in their own right, as you would if reading for another person. The natural tendency is to avoid any suggestion that what one does not wish to see may be present in the reading: the conscious mind rejecting what might be unpleasant in the unconscious. However, if you approach a reading for yourself with the same seriousness and sense of respect with which you would a reading for another, the results can be stunning. When faced with a difficult reading for oneself, it can be useful to select certain cards from the rest of the deck that would be helpful in understanding or resolving the difficulty. Lay these 'helping' cards next to the 'difficult' ones and meditate on the interaction between them. This can produce surprising new insights and fresh perspective on seemingly insolvable matters.

When experimenting with readings for yourself, you can enjoy formulating your own layout designs. Use your favourite numbers or personal sense of pattern to help devise the structure. Some people like precise readings that require a specific question such as the Twenty-one Card Spread figured opposite, while others may prefer looser structures, such as the Fifteen Card Spread. The Gypsy Spread calls for forty-two cards and is not generally recommended for beginners. The loose structure and large number of cards required can easily cause 'psychic indigestion' and can be quite daunting. However, as you become more experienced you might like to experiment with it.

It is a good idea to practice with the various readings for yourself to discover which you feel most comfortable with before trying out

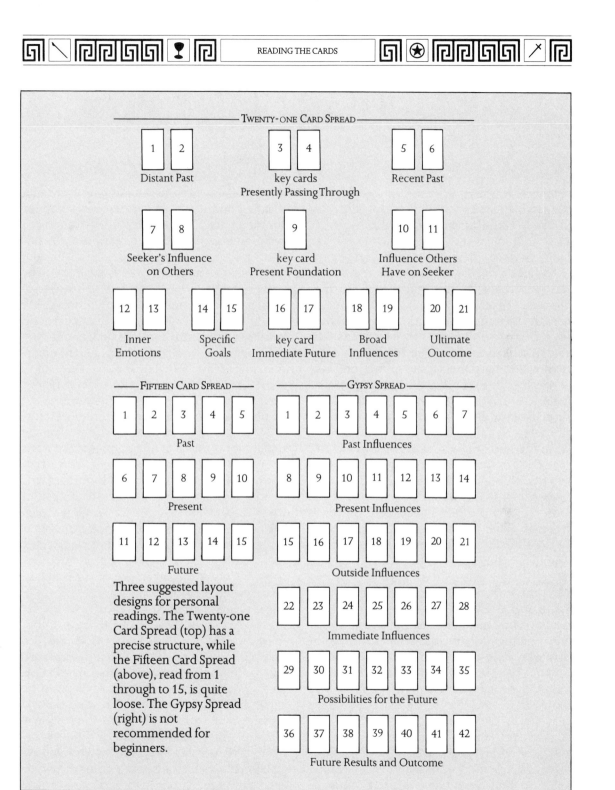

TWENTY-ONE CARD SPREAD

| 1 | 2 | | 3 | 4 | | 5 | 6 |

Distant Past | key cards Presently Passing Through | Recent Past

| 7 | 8 | | 9 | | 10 | 11 |

Seeker's Influence on Others | key card Present Foundation | Influence Others Have on Seeker

| 12 | 13 | | 14 | 15 | | 16 | 17 | | 18 | 19 | | 20 | 21 |

Inner Emotions | Specific Goals | key card Immediate Future | Broad Influences | Ultimate Outcome

FIFTEEN CARD SPREAD

| 1 | 2 | 3 | 4 | 5 |
Past

| 6 | 7 | 8 | 9 | 10 |
Present

| 11 | 12 | 13 | 14 | 15 |
Future

GYPSY SPREAD

| 1 | 2 | 3 | 4 | 5 | 6 | 7 |
Past Influences

| 8 | 9 | 10 | 11 | 12 | 13 | 14 |
Present Influences

| 15 | 16 | 17 | 18 | 19 | 20 | 21 |
Outside Influences

| 22 | 23 | 24 | 25 | 26 | 27 | 28 |
Immediate Influences

| 29 | 30 | 31 | 32 | 33 | 34 | 35 |
Possibilities for the Future

| 36 | 37 | 38 | 39 | 40 | 41 | 42 |
Future Results and Outcome

Three suggested layout designs for personal readings. The Twenty-one Card Spread (top) has a precise structure, while the Fifteen Card Spread (above), read from 1 through to 15, is quite loose. The Gypsy Spread (right) is not recommended for beginners.

readings with friends. You will quickly discover which layout and number of cards you find most stimulating to work with.

Reading the Tarot for Others

It is not the task of the Tarot reader to advise the seeker exactly what to do, but rather to read the meanings of the images laid out. The seeker can then interpret these meanings as he or she wishes. It may be tempting to give advice in all manner of dilemmas, but save suggesting the seeker look more deeply into his or her psyche for answers, direct advice should be avoided. I will not, for instance, allow myself to be drawn into the 'Should I leave my husband and marry the milkman?' kind of question. A Tarot reader should act as a guide, aiding the seeker to find his or her own conclusions. If a seeker should need more help than can be offered during a reading, I would suggest counselling or psychotherapy, and to keep a list of therapists and counselling agencies on hand. Confidentiality is another important point to remember. It is imperative that you do not gossip about what has been revealed during a reading, or use any information gained in any way which might prove embarrassing or damaging to your seeker.

Many people approach a Tarot reader at times of personal crisis or indecision. You therefore need to be able to listen as well as talk. When anyone is in a state of stress or conflict, they tend to be more impressionable and vulnerable than usual. This puts the Tarot reader in a position of some power, which must on no account be misused. There is always a danger of the self-fulfilling prophecy, that is, a prediction which the seeker takes so seriously that he unconsciously makes it come true. For example, I heard recently of a Tarot reader who 'predicted' a road accident which might result in the seeker's death. The seeker shrugged it off at the time, laughingly remarking, 'So much the better'; however, six months later he drove his car too fast around a dangerous bend and was killed outright. Whether this was a result of his inner conviction that he would die in a car accident is something we will never know. Nevertheless, such negative comment on the part of the reader was, in my own opinion, unforgivable. This is not to say that any mention of difficulties must be avoided. On the contrary, it seems to be the case that a reader's acknowledgement of difficulties the seeker is currently experiencing can be very useful. But some potentially helpful focus should also always be acknowledged. The fact that troubles and fears can be openly discussed is therapeutic in itself, and while a hard-and-fast solution to a particular problem is not necessarily called for, the opportunity for open discussion is helpful.

Becoming a skilled Tarot reader is something which will require a good deal of practice and effort on your part. It will involve a lot of trial and error as you seek to develop your own particular style. You will need to experiment with different layouts and ways of looking at the cards until you settle upon a method which suits you best. It is important to decide at first how professional, or how casual, you want to be when doing readings. Personally, I feel it is best to set aside a certain amount of time for each reading – I allow an hour – and to make formal appointments. It is tempting to be cajoled into reading, say at parties, often for a number of people; but noise and background chatter are not conducive to the workings of the intuition.

Even if you do not wish to charge for readings, it is still preferable to make proper appointments. Experience will dictate what is appropriate for you and what is not. The more seriously you approach your readings, however, the more seriously other people will react to you. Many readers allow a quiet time for 'clearing the mind' before starting a reading and some practise relaxation breathing exercises. Many readers like to establish a particular ritual of sitting in the same chair and using the same table and a special cloth to lay the Tarot cards on.

The method used for shuffling and dealing the cards is another matter for personal preference. Some readers let their seekers shuffle the deck and then deal from the top. I shuffle myself, preferring that others do not handle my cards; I then lay the cards out, face down, and invite the seeker to select however many cards the spread calls for. This is something with which you can experiment until you find the method that suits you best. Some readers read reversed cards. That is, if the card appears upside down in a reading, they read the usual divinatory meaning in reverse. This is a practice which I do not follow, because I consider that each card has both a positive and negative expression in its upright position anyway. It depends upon its position in the spread and the 'weight' of the surrounding cards as to which interpretation would be most appropriate. Again, however, this is a matter for personal preference.

We will now turn our attention to examining a number of layouts and sample readings. The samples also have blank spreads which you might like to photocopy for your file. For each of your own readings fill in the blanks of the cards selected at the reading, the date, the seeker's name and the question the seeker came with. Make notes on the reading. They will come in useful so that you may check up on progress the next time the seeker consults you. I usually allow at least six months to elapse between readings.

All the examples that follow are genuine cases and I am most grateful to all those who gave me permission to use them here. A useful exercise in comparison of style and interpretation would be to read the 'case history' and look at the spread before reading my interpretation. Try to interpret each reading for yourself first, imagining the seeker, whose situation is briefly described, were coming to you for the reading. Make your own notes on what you think this reading reveals and perhaps what alternative courses of action each spread suggests. Then compare my interpretation with your own.

THE HOROSCOPE

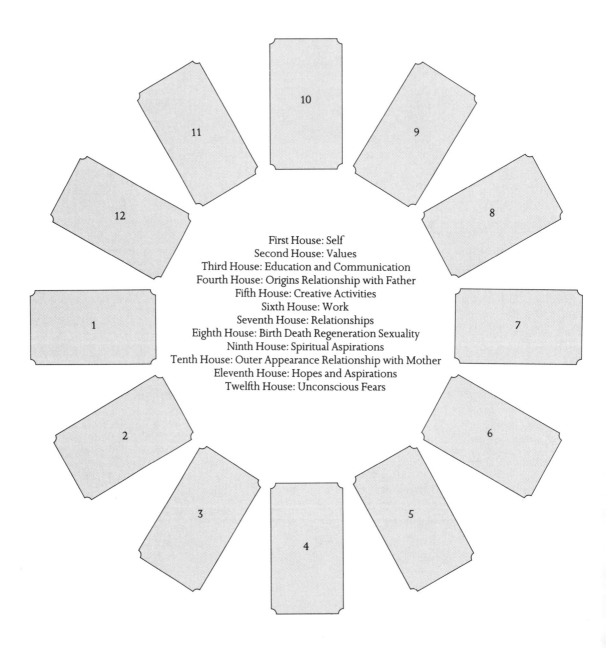

First House: Self
Second House: Values
Third House: Education and Communication
Fourth House: Origins Relationship with Father
Fifth House: Creative Activities
Sixth House: Work
Seventh House: Relationships
Eighth House: Birth Death Regeneration Sexuality
Ninth House: Spiritual Aspirations
Tenth House: Outer Appearance Relationship with Mother
Eleventh House: Hopes and Aspirations
Twelfth House: Unconscious Fears

The first spread to be examined is the Horoscope. For those students who are familiar with astrology, the layout will be instantly recognisable as the zodiacal houses. This is a good spread to use when looking at all areas of a seeker's life, as the twelve houses and twelve cards give clear indications of what is at work in each area of life at the time. The whole deck should be used.

POSITION ONE

The First House: this is the position of Self, how one appears to others and the kind of outward personality one reveals to the rest of the world. Astrologically, this house is that of the Ascendant.

POSITION TWO

The Second House: this is the card of values, what one prizes, how one goes about obtaining what is important, whether it be money, possessions or anything else rated valuable.

POSITION THREE

The Third House: this card indicates the intellect, the workings of the mind, education and communication.

POSITION FOUR

The Fourth House: this card reveals something about the origins of the seeker and often suggests the relationship the seeker had with his or her father.

POSITION FIVE

The Fifth House: this card represents creativity and pleasure. This position also covers love affairs and children.

POSITION SIX

The Sixth House: this card reflects the work and service in which the seeker is engaged.

POSITION SEVEN

The Seventh House: this card will indicate the kind of relationships and partnerships prevailing at the time of the reading.

POSITION EIGHT

The Eighth House: this card will represent attitudes towards the unconscious mind, death, rebirth and sexuality.

POSITION NINE

The Ninth House: this card will reflect the kind of spiritual aspirations the seeker has. It may also suggest foreign travel or higher education.

POSITION TEN

The Tenth House: this card will indicate the way the world perceives the seeker and may also reflect the way the seeker experiences or relates to his or her mother.

POSITION ELEVEN

The Eleventh House: this card reflects the seeker's hopes and aspirations in relation to society as a whole, and the seeker's place in it.

POSITION TWELVE

The Twelfth House: this card may reflect unconscious fears or hidden worries. It may also suggest restrictions or limitations.

Let us examine the Horoscope layout for Joanna M.

Joanna M, aged thirty-one years, came for a Tarot reading because she wanted to know how her new work-life would turn out. She was starting a new study in psychology, a complete switch from the successful business career she was then pursuing. She had chosen psychology partly because she wanted a change of direction, being tired of the highly commercial world she occupied at the time, and partly because she had a real phobia about snakes. She felt that her phobia must derive from some underlying cause, and hoped that her studies in psychology would help her understand it.

Her family background was neither easy nor happy: her father had left her mother before Jo was born, leaving Jo with strong feelings of rejection and disappointment which she did not like to face. Her mother's career was curtailed by Jo's birth and her unachieved aims and ambitions were thus later projected onto her daughter. It appears that Jo had realised many of her mother's long-cherished wishes through her successful business career, but now wanted to change direction. And she particularly wanted to understand the relevance of her snake phobia. The Horoscope reading went as follows:

POSITION ONE
The First House: the Star

The presence of the Star in the House of Self indicates that no matter how many unpleasant obstacles present themselves, Jo will always manage to maintain an attitude of optimism and hope. Jo connected the 'spites' which flew out of Pandora's box with her fear of snakes. She is convinced that her most important task is to understand and restrain her phobia before she can really progress on an inner level; but she is hopeful that her prospective studies, which may include personal therapy, will help her overcome her fears. She liked the image of the Star, with its implication that Hope did not fly away.

POSITION TWO
The Second House: Queen of Cups

The Queen of Cups appeared in the Second House, the position of values. A look at Jo's natal horoscope revealed that her Sun and Venus were in Scorpio in the Second House, at the time of her birth. It thus seemed appropriate to find the Queen of Cups, the card which expresses Scorpio energy, in that house. Until recently, Jo admitted that she valued her intellectual capacity over her feelings. Now, however, her search for self-understanding has brought her to value her feelings and to take them more seriously. The Queen of Cups reflects the opportunity to examine the feeling nature in some depth. The arms of her throne are decorated with golden snakes, symbol of Scorpio. The snake is traditionally associated with sexuality; it is also a symbol of death and rebirth; and the periodic shedding of its own skin suggests the capacity for regeneration. This signified that Jo's phobia of snakes might take her to a deeper level of understanding, perhaps to a valuing of something she currently fears.

POSITION THREE
The Third House: Judgement

The placement of Judgement in the position of education and communication seemed to

reflect the changes of Jo's interests. Hermes in the Judgement card is not simply the teacher or god concerned with intellectual communication. He also functions as the mysterious Psychopomp, guide of souls. He effects communication between the conscious and unconscious mind, providing a channel whereby an understanding of unconscious material is made conscious. Judgement also reveals a time for evaluation, and Jo felt this to be particularly relevant, given her current in-depth examination of her life. Although she is successful in her career and in other material ways, she feels this is no longer sufficient. She would like to explore avenues which take her into deeper personal understanding, in the hope that they might make her life richer and more satisfying. Hermes in the card of Judgement calls the dead to rise and be accounted for: that which has lain fallow must now be brought to life.

POSITION FOUR
The Fourth House: Three of Swords
The Three of Swords in the house describing her origins, and in particular her relationship with her father, touched Jo deeply. She felt it an apt image, since she is currently beginning to understand how much she hates and resents her father for having deserted her mother and herself. Until fairly recently, Jo felt it 'wrong' not to love a parent, even a parent who had let her down. She had repressed her anger towards her father and substituted a 'phoney forgiveness', as she put it. She maintained this attitude of 'forgiveness' towards her unknown father until her reunion with him during her adolescence. She

then adopted a polite, coolly friendly contact with him, never acknowledging how much pain was still attached to their relationship. As she is now beginning to accept her pain, she feels that a real relationship might eventually be born. When looking at the image on the Three of Swords, Jo felt that in fantasy she needed to 'kill' her father to punish him for 'killing' her through rejection. She felt that if she could hate him at last, there might, in time, be a cleared path for some kind of love to slowly begin to grow. The poison needed to be drained before any healing could occur.

POSITION FIVE
The Fifth House: Eight of Wands
The house of creativity and pleasure was well-aspected by the clear skies and seas of the Eight of Wands. The smooth progress of Jason's ship reminded Jo of how well things were going for her creatively. Not only had she been accepted into a highly reputable institution for further education, she was also studying subjects, including astrology, for her own pleasure. This card seemed a bright cheerful light, contrasting the more painful areas of deep emotion she was experiencing.

POSITION SIX
The Sixth House: Ace of Pentacles
The Sixth House is connected with work and career prospects, so the Ace of Pentacles bringing sudden financial good fortune was well placed. Jo had just received news that a full grant for three years' study would be paid. What was more, she had been offered a temporary job which would tide her over until her course started, and this job was

extremely lucrative. The Ace of Pentacles certainly seemed to be fulfilling its promise of financial stability in Jo's case.

<hr>

POSITION SEVEN

The Seventh House: Four of Pentacles
The Seventh House is connected with relationships with other people. The appearance of the Four of Pentacles revealed a reluctance within Jo about letting go and risking change. She said she had concentrated all her energies on her work: 'Work is my most significant partner.' She sought security through financial independence, not feeling secure enough inside herself to trust anyone else to care for her. She finds it difficult to trust anything which is not guaranteed, and so tends not to get involved in emotional relationships because they are too risky. Being without the important father figure for most of her early life, she decided, at an early age, that the only way to be taken care of financially was to take care of herself. Now she cannot let herself go, even if she wants to.

<hr>

POSITION EIGHT

The Eighth House: Five of Swords
The Five of Swords is the card in which Apollo, the father god, appears to Orestes, indicating that it is time for him to face his fate. The Eighth House concentrates on the fundamental issues of life: sex, birth, death and regeneration. Astrologically it is the house ruled by Scorpio and so governs all the aspects with which Scorpio is connected. The appearance of the Five of Swords seems to be telling Jo to accept her limitations, accept her fate, and accept her father in all his negative aspects, before she can be free. On an unconscious level, she may be afraid of close, intimate contact with men, for fear of rejection. This may manifest itself as a fear of snakes, concealing her real fear of an intimate contact which might leave her vulnerable. Jo needs to carefully examine these sensitive areas in an effort to reveal what might be hidden in her unconscious.

<hr>

POSITION NINE

The Ninth House: the World
The Ninth House is connected with a search for meaning, a desire for higher education or spiritual knowledge. The World stands as a symbol of Jo's achievement in completing the first stage of her aspirations. Her acceptance into a prestigious university, along with a handsome grant, symbolises public acknowledgement of her value. Through her hard work and effort, she has earned the crown of attainment suggested by the World. The dancing figure will become the Fool once again when she starts her course. Thus there is the promise of another crown when she has successfully completed her studies.

<hr>

POSITION TEN

The Tenth House: Queen of Swords
The Tenth House is connected with the way the world perceives us, and also with our relationship to the mother. The Queen of Swords reminded Jo very much of her own mother, strong-willed and ambitious, but cold. Jo felt she had absorbed many of her mother's characteristics. The myth of Atalanta touched her deeply, for her mother would have liked a boy and even gave her a boyish

nickname. Jo felt that for her mother she had to achieve a great deal of prestige and success in order to compensate for her existence, as well as to impress her father. She hoped she could avoid taking things to the extremes displayed by Atalanta in the myth, but certainly felt that her unsatisfactory relationship with men had much to do with her mother's own disappointment. Although Jo was initially unwanted by both her parents, she felt she became a vehicle for their unlived dreams and ambitions. Now she wants to start living for herself.

POSITION ELEVEN
The Eleventh House: Ten of Pentacles
The Eleventh House describes hopes and aspirations, as well as an opportunity to develop personal values and project them into society at large. Jo hopes to marry and have children one day. She would like to start her own family, based on happier foundations than those she herself experienced. She feels the need to establish traditions which can be carried on in her family. She would like to see the development of something good and lasting, which, unlike her own

unhappy inheritance, could be positively passed down through generations. She feels her family was 'cursed' and would like an opportunity to heal those wounds. The appearance of the Ten of Pentacles gave her a definite sense of encouragement.

POSITION TWELVE
The Twelfth House: the Sun
In the Twelfth House, the house of unconscious and hidden matters, the appearance of the Sun showed Apollo in a friendly light, unlike his stern exterior in the Five of Swords. In the eighth card, he seemed harsh and unrelenting. In the Sun, however, he suggests that if Jo can carry out the tasks he demanded in the Five of Swords, she will benefit from his brilliant light and warm rays. If she is brave enough to carry out his bidding, she can then expect Apollo's illumination of her hidden difficulties and thus break the restrictions which have imprisoned her. The Twelfth House is traditionally associated with prisons. Jo felt that, like Orestes, she was imprisoned by her family's fate. She hoped that by using the inner image of Apollo, she might release herself from her ill-fated family line.

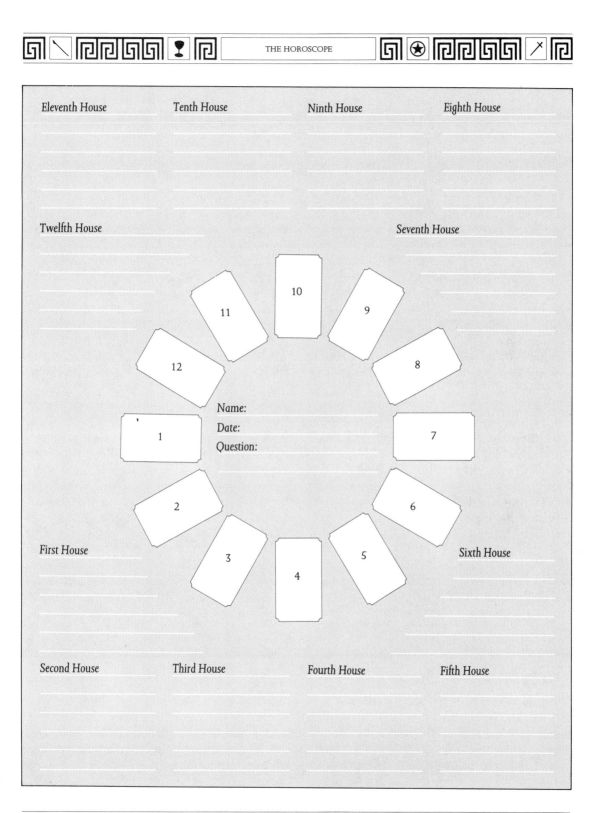

Eleventh House

Tenth House

Ninth House

Eighth House

Twelfth House

Seventh House

Name:
Date:
Question:

First House

Sixth House

Second House

Third House

Fourth House

Fifth House

THE TEN CARD HORSESHOE

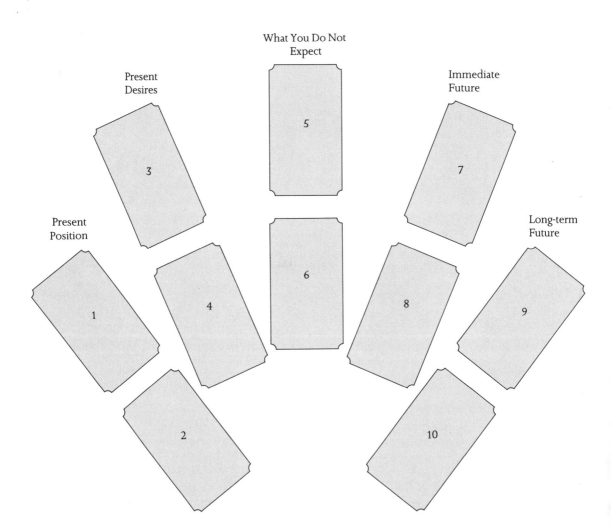

Present Desires

What You Do Not Expect

Immediate Future

Present Position

Long-term Future

The second layout we shall look at is the Ten Card Horseshoe. This is an interesting spread as it covers the seeker's present situation, and can also reveal what is unexpected, thus providing an additional perspective on the future. This spread can be shortened to only five cards, or lengthened to fifteen. If you use fifteen cards, the first five cards laid down represent the past, the second five the present, and the last five, the future. The meanings of the positions remain the same. The whole deck should be used.

Present Position: these cards reflect the circumstances prevailing in the seeker's life.

POSITION THREE AND FOUR
Present Desires: these cards reflect the seeker's present wishes and wants.

POSITION FIVE AND SIX
What You Do Not Expect: these cards reveal influences looming in the seeker's life which he or she does not expect.

POSITION SEVEN AND EIGHT
Immediate Future: these cards reflect what is likely to happen in the near future, that is within one–two months of the reading.

POSITION NINE AND TEN
Long-term Future: these cards indicate possibilities for the next six–twelve months.

We shall look in greater depth at the workings of this spread as we examine the reading for Felicity F.

Felicity F, aged twenty-six years, came to see me with a complex problem regarding her relationship with her parents, her forthcoming marriage and the fact that she had recently become pregnant. Felicity has a very comfortless relationship with both her parents, but more especially with her mother, who never wished to have Felicity and arranged an abortion but left the operation too late. She had brought her daughter into the world with the intention of having the baby adopted. In the end, however, the maternal grandmother assumed the task of bringing up the child. Felicity experienced a push-pull existence between her parents and grandmother. From time to time her parents would decide to have her with them but then would return her suddenly to grandmother. Felicity now harbours fiercely hostile feelings towards her mother. She was terrified of letting her mother know she was pregnant and about to get married, lest she appeared at

the wedding 'like the thirteenth fairy in the Sleeping Beauty, who puts a spell on everything'. At the same time, however, Felicity displayed an unwitting ambivalence in her behaviour by arranging for the wedding to be held in her home town. We viewed the Ten Card Horseshoe reading as follows:

POSITION ONE AND TWO
Present Position: the Fool and the Tower
The presence of the Fool and the Tower together in the Present Position seemed to indicate that a great deal of energy was constellating and needed expression. The Fool, standing outside the maternal cave and poised to jump into the unknown, reflects Felicity's present position. She states that she wishes no contact with her parents, yet she is clearly still very attached to them, albeit contrarily. Her hateful feelings are keeping her tied to the maternal cave. The Tower symbolises the elaborate labyrinth con-

structed to hide something shameful. After some discussion, it transpired that Felicity feels deeply ashamed of having such uncaring parents. She feels that it has somehow been her fault, that she was unlovable and therefore deserved to be treated in such a fashion. She assumed the burden of guilt from her parents and felt it to be her own transgression. The hideous Minotaur within the laby-rinth is the guilt which she has been feeding with hatred. She is concerned that the murderous feelings she is experiencing towards her mother might damage her unborn child, yet she wants to make sure that her own unhappy experiences will not be repeated. In wanting to keep her mother away from the baby, Felicity also wants to protect the baby from her own rage.

POSITION THREE AND FOUR
Present Desires: Knight of Pentacles and Nine of Swords

The Knight of Pentacles appears in the place of Present Desires as a wish to unravel the complex problem. The myth of Aristaeus was helpful here. When Aristaeus found that his precious bees were all dying, he went to great lengths to ascertain the reason. First, he learned that the only one who could tell him was the old sea-god, Proteus. The next problem was to find Proteus and hold onto him despite all his transformations and shifting guises. Proteus turned himself into a tree, a lion, a panther, fire and running water. The important thing for Aristaeus was not to be intimidated by these various apparitions. Aristaeus was finally rewarded for his efforts. Felicity must be equally tenacious if she is to find a way of coming to terms with her family relationships. She must, like the Knight of Pentacles, work her way thoroughly through various different emotions before coming to a resolution and peace of mind.

The Nine of Swords indicates that she is still tormented with guilt. This guilt, evoked by the Furies within, stems from the murderous rage she feels towards her mother. While she continues to shoulder the burden of guilt for her parents, she will not be able to free herself from the all-consuming hatred she is currently experiencing.

POSITION FIVE AND SIX
What You Do Not Expect: Four of Wands and Queen of Cups

The joy and sense of achievement indicated by the Four of Wands was certainly not something Felicity could imagine at the time of the reading. She was so caught up in her negative spiral that she could not visualise a time when she would release herself from it by hard, creative effort. Yet the Four of Wands, accompanied by the Queen of Cups, suggests that the necessary contact with her own deeper aspirations is not as far away as she might expect. One of the problems was Felicity's ambivalence about her parents attending the wedding. Consciously, she does not want them there, but she continues to worry about the matter. She is determined to hold the ceremony in their small home town and wants to invite her grandmother, knowing that her parents will thus learn what is happening. It would seem therefore that on some unconscious level, she does want her parents to be there. If she were able to contact her true feelings, which lie buried beneath all the guilt and anger, she might be able to decide what she would genuinely like to do. The two cards, although indeed unexpected, indicate that she might manage to achieve such clarity.

POSITION SEVEN AND EIGHT
Immediate Future: Ace of Wands and Queen of Pentacles

The Ace of Wands, presided over by the great Zeus, indicates an upsurge of creative energy and a conviction that new beginnings can provide a basis for future life. The Ace of Wands often marks a turning point, and the emergence of new and vital energy furnishes courage and enthusiasm to face up to changes. The Queen of Pentacles indicates the need to take care of oneself; one's bodily

needs and emotional well-being. Although Felicity's inner experience of care has been mostly neglect, she must now assume the task of being a nurturing mother to herself. She cannot rely on her actual mother to do it for her; and as she is soon to become a mother herself, she needs a good deal of strength to face her new and challenging role. The Queen of Pentacles is an image of earthy sensuality, prepared to take seriously the task of caring for the body. She can therefore be an image of great value to Felicity at the moment. The influence of the creative, optimistic, energetic Ace of Wands, and the stable, earthy, sensual wisdom offered by the Queen of Pentacles, could prove most beneficial in Felicity's future struggles.

─────── POSITION NINE AND TEN ───────

Long-term Future: the Lovers and Three of Cups

The Lovers is a card of choice and stresses the importance of conscious decision-making. Given Felicity's dread of her mother appearing at her wedding like the 'thirteenth fairy' and spoiling everything, the background to the myth of the Lovers card seemed especially relevant. The circumstances preceding the

judgement of Paris involved a huge wedding feast to which all the gods and goddesses on Olympus were invited – all, that is, except Eris, the goddess of discord. But although uninvited, Eris arrived at the celebrations in a furious rage, throwing into the assembly a golden apple and crying, 'This belongs to the fairest.' She knew it would immediately upset the happy occasion. As we saw in the Lovers, three goddesses caught the apple together and each refused to relinquish her claim. Paris was commanded to choose only one goddess and the end result was the Trojan War. Felicity's anxiety about her mother's presence at her wedding obviously needs careful examination. A number of considered choices are open to her. Felicity must face up to the options concerning attendance at her wedding and the start of her new life. She must take into account all the possible consequences of each choice. Once she has made her choice, she can proceed to enjoy the celebrations to the full, as indicated by the Three of Cups. This card signifies a joyful occasion, an important event. Felicity must be as explicit as possible about her feelings so that she can enjoy her special day without unnecessary stress.

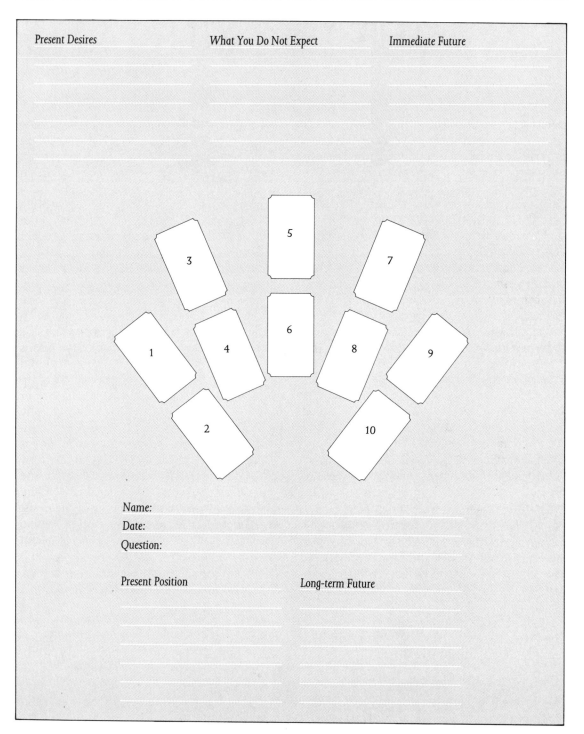

Present Desires

What You Do Not Expect

Immediate Future

Name:

Date:

Question:

Present Position

Long-term Future

THE TRIANGLE

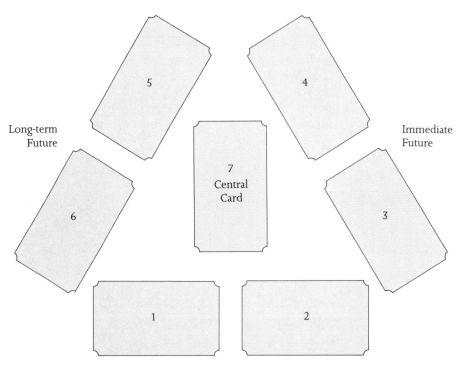

Long-term
Future

Immediate
Future

7
Central
Card

Present Position

The third layout we shall look at is the Triangle. This seven-card spread is useful for answering fairly specific questions, as it gives an idea of present and future influences. The important card to watch is the central card, which has most weight in the reading.

POSITION ONE AND TWO

The Present Position: the seeker's situation in his or her life at the time of the reading.

POSITION THREE AND FOUR

The Immediate Future: this placement describes what influences the seeker can expect

to prevail in the immediate future, that is in the next one to three months.

POSITION FIVE AND SIX

The Long-term Future: what the seeker can expect during the next six to twelve months.

POSITION SEVEN

The Central Card: the card which influences all the others. This card is fundamental to the reading and its effect is considerable.

We will examine this spread now in more detail for Jonathan D.

Jonathan D, aged forty-six years, a successful business man, came to see me about the prospects of changing his career. He had previously worked in the world of commerce but had recently been offered an opportunity to become involved in a film project. It would entail risking a lot of capital, and possibly, his respectable city image as well. On the other hand, he had always been drawn to the glamour of the film industry. Nevertheless, the venture would be alien to his conservative family background and would, as he put it, 'shock many of my staid friends'. Moreover, the film in question would be a controversial one. All the same,

Jonathan was very attracted to the idea and wanted to see what the cards had to reveal on the matter. He drew the following seven cards and we laid out the Triangle.

—————— POSITION ONE AND TWO ——————
Present Position: the Emperor and Nine of Pentacles

The Emperor in the Present Position revealed Jonathan's solid, stable, materially secure status. He is a successful business man with an excellent capacity for shrewd financial judgements. He could easily turn his sharp wits to commercial advantage. The problem is that the ease of his life is beginning to bore him.

He longs to be extended by something more elusive and adventurous, but is understandably nervous lest he prove inadequate to the risk. The Nine of Pentacles indicates the extent of his current financial security as a result of past effort. He could easily relax and enjoy the fruits of his labours. The drawback is that security in itself no longer satisfies him. He married young, his two children are grown up and have left home. He feels it is a good time to branch out and take a chance.

--- POSITION THREE AND FOUR ---
Immediate Future: Seven of Pentacles and Ace of Wands

The Seven of Pentacles reveals the choice that has to be made between adhering to known values or risking everything on a whim. The Seven depicts Daedalus in the position of having to choose between remaining loyal to Minos, or switching allegiance to Pasiphae, whose request was stamped with the mark of the god Poseidon. Jonathan could well identify with that image. The Ace of Wands, however, indicates an upsurge of fiery enthusiasm and energy for a new venture, which might counteract the risk. Jonathan obviously has quite a bit to lose, but there also appears to be a lot to gain, especially through the achievement of creative satisfaction.

--- POSITION FIVE AND SIX ---
Long-term Future: Seven of Swords and Six of Wands

The Seven of Swords warns that Jonathan should be especially prudent in his handling of the transaction in question. He will have to move carefully, even cunningly, in order not to lose everything. The Seven of Swords indicates the need for tact and diplomacy and discreet management of one's affairs. The Six of Wands, however, reveals a sense of triumph and victory which suggests that Jonathan may be very successful in his new venture, despite the difficulties.

--- POSITION SEVEN ---
The Central Card: the Fool

The Fool placed in the centre of the Triangle indicates the overall influence pervading the spread. In this case, the adventurous, risk-taking spirit of the Fool seems to suggest that Jonathan will take the leap into the unknown world of film, regardless of what else is at stake. Controversial though his new life might be, his old life will probably restrict him more than he can bear. Jonathan did not yet know if his move would, indeed, prove 'foolish', but he is strongly tempted to give it a chance. The spirit of adventure which the Fool embodies is hard to ignore.

THE TRIANGLE

Long-term Future

Immediate Future

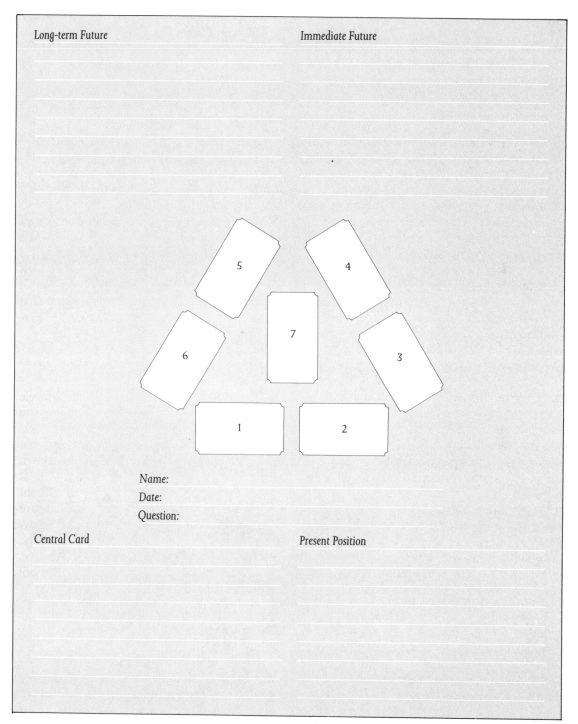

Name:
Date:
Question:

Central Card

Present Position

THE STAR

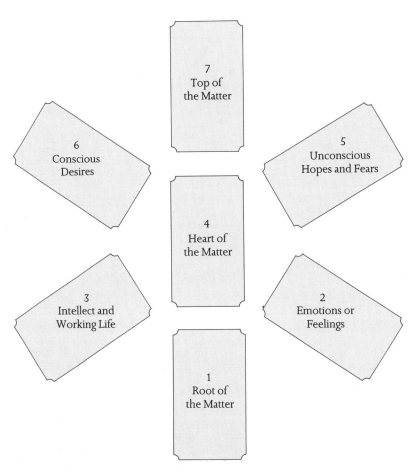

7
Top of
the Matter

6
Conscious
Desires

5
Unconscious
Hopes and Fears

4
Heart of
the Matter

3
Intellect and
Working Life

2
Emotions or
Feelings

1
Root of
the Matter

The fourth layout we shall look at is the Star. This seven-card layout is useful for understanding both the inner and outer influences operating in a person's life. It highlights the problems and potentials prevailing at a given moment; examination of which can be most helpful. I often use only the Minor Arcana for one reading of the Star spread, and then only the Major for another.

The Minor spread conveys an impression of the practical factors at work, while the Major spread can offer a valuable insight into the psychological position of the seeker.

—————— POSITION ONE ——————
The Root of the Matter: this position describes the present situation of the seeker; what is difficult or helpful at the time.

POSITION TWO

The Feelings or Emotions: this describes the current state of affairs with regard to the seeker's relationships and love life. It also reflects his or her emotional state at the time of the reading.

POSITION THREE

The Intellect and Working Life: this position reflects the seeker's attitude to work and career. It also indicates how his or her mind is functioning.

POSITION FOUR

The Heart of the Matter: this is the card around which the whole reading revolves. It is the most significant card in the spread and often reveals the true problem or solution.

POSITION FIVE

Unconscious Hopes and Fears: this position reflects hidden material that is just beginning to surface. The seeker may be only dimly aware of these new forces at work.

POSITION SIX

Conscious Desires: this position reveals what the seeker really wants, and is aware of wanting.

POSITION SEVEN

The Top of the Matter: this position reveals the present conceivable outcome.

We shall now look at two readings for Lucy B., one using only the Minor cards and the other using the Major Arcana.

Lucy B, aged thirty-five years, recently divorced, came for a reading to ask for help in her divorce settlement. Her fifteen-year-long marriage had come to an abrupt end, her husband leaving without warning to live with another woman. This had coincided with the birth of Lucy's third child. At the time of the reading, she was very concerned about the outcome of the financial settlement. Her husband appeared reluctant to agree to what she considered fair. Her questions also related to her ability to start a new career, so that she could in time become financially independent and support her children without having to rely totally upon her husband' income.

Reading with the Minor Arcana

POSITION ONE

The Root of the Matter: Ace of Pentacles
The Ace of Pentacles in the Root of the Matter augured well for an advantageous resolution to the financial wrangle. The Ace of Pentacles suggested receipt of a lump sum. It also suggested that Lucy had enough raw energy available to apply herself to material achievement. She had previously demonstrated considerable talent in the design field, but had not pursued a career while devoting her time to raising children. The appearance of the Ace of Pentacles indicated a very real capacity for resuming her former activity.

POSITION TWO

Feelings or Emotions: Four of Cups

The Four of Cups in the position of feelings reflected Lucy's shock and dismay at finding her hitherto peaceful world shattered by the discovery that her husband was not the man she believed him to be. The Four of Cups signifies dissatisfaction, depression and a sense of being let down or betrayed. Lucy did indeed feel bitterly let down by her husband's abandonment of her. At the same time, she agreed that she had ignored or blinded herself to many warning signs through the years. She had not wanted to see or confront any of the underlyng problems in their relationship. Like Psyche in the myth reflected by the Cups, she had lived a charmed life. She relied totally on her hus-

band to provide a beautiful home and life-style, but never questioned his personal needs or wishes too closely. She did not want to know that everything in their garden might not be rosy.

POSITION THREE

Intellect and Working Life: Nine of Cups

The Nine of Cups in the position of her working life seemed positive, given her plans to further a career in design. The Nine of Cups is known as the 'wish' card and signifies the fulfilment of a dream or wish held dear. It represents rewards for efforts made, and emotional, as well as material stability is indicated. Although the Cups often refer to emotional matters, the card in this reading fell in the position of work. It thus reflected Lucy's wish to find independence and satis-faction through her own skill, and suggested that if she was confident in her ambition, she would achieve success.

POSITION FOUR

The Heart of the Matter: Eight of Pentacles

The Eight of Pentacles suggests that a period of hard work and struggle is needed to acquire or perfect a skill. It is the card of the apprentice and often denotes a 'second-time-around' apprentice, rather than say, the school leaver or novice. In the myth of Daedalus, the stage depicted by the Eight of Pentacles showed him as having lost every-thing yet, undaunted, starting again from the beginning. This card in the central position shows that Lucy may well find greater interest and pleasure in a new field of work, despite the fact that she must start anew.

POSITION FIVE

Unconscious Hopes or Fears: Five of Wands

The Five of Wands in the sphere of uncon-scious hopes or fears, warns Lucy that a material struggle will ensue if she over-stretches herself. Like Jason, she must over-come the dragon of material pressures in order to attain her goal, and she must recognise the limitations of her situation as well as its positive implications. She admitted that by nature she was inclined to rush headlong into projects, and had had many business disasters as a result of ignoring difficulties. She recognised how vital it was that she curb her impetuosity, for she would not now have a husband to sort out her messes. It was more important to create a stable family life for her children.

POSITION SIX

Conscious Desires: Page of Wands

The Page of Wands in the position of con-scious desires suggests the stirring of new creative potential, for the Page of Wands acts as a forerunner to the birth of new creative endeavour. Like all the Pages, he is fragile and needs much nurturing to bring his seeds to fruition. Lucy should cherish her ideas and allow her creativity plenty of scope. She needs space and time for her imagination to expand and develop to its fullest potential.

POSITION SEVEN

The Top of the Matter: Five of Cups

The Five of Cups suggests that though Lucy has experienced much bitter disappointment and regret over past actions, as symbolised by the overturned cups, something workable

still stands. This might indicate that something can be salvaged from the ruins of the marital relationship, or that some strength remains in her that is capable of further development. She needs to accept both the

despair and anguish at the end of her marriage and yet be aware of the positive possibilities still left intact. Lucy agreed that new aspects of herself were now beginning to emerge as a result of the crisis.

Reading with the Major Arcana

POSITION ONE
The Root of the Matter: the Hermit
The Hermit at the Root of the Matter indicated that, on an inner level, Lucy needs plenty of time and introspection to fully absorb the traumatic events of the past year. The Hermit is the card of 'time healing wounds' and suggests the need for patience. Cronus is said to be waiting patiently for his Golden Age to return. The Hermit also teaches lessons of solitude and if Lucy can withstand the temptation to avoid being alone for a while, she will come to terms with her situation and receive the great benefits the Hermit can offer. His is a card which signifies the need for self-discovery and self-knowledge.

POSITION TWO
Feelings or Emotions: Temperance
Temperance in the sphere of feelings indicates Lucy's need to allow full expression of all her various and conflicting emotions. She is torn between sheer hatred for her ex-husband's actions, bitterness regarding his behaviour towards her and the children and, at the same time, affection and wistful longing

for the love they once shared. She finds it difficult to accept that, on the one hand, she hates him and never wants to see him again and, on the other, longs desperately to get him back. The image of Temperance suggests that mixing and blending the conflicting emotions is the best way ultimately to achieve some semblance of harmony. There also needs to be some form of communication between herself and her ex-husband lest matters become worse.

POSITION THREE
Intellect and Working Life: Justice
Justice in the position of Intellect shows the need for a balanced mind and clear perspective. Justice and Temperance are found together, which suggests the possibility of achieving a balance of emotions, and the execution of practical arrangements. Justice gives Lucy a clear mind and the ability to look at her situation coolly and practically. Justice involves fairness, and Lucy insists that she only wants what is her reasonable right. She wants to come to a decision within herself about what is just and what is not. The clarity of vision which Justice offers can help her to deal lucidly with the settlement, as well as to be pragmatic in her new business plans.

────── POSITION FOUR ──────

The Heart of the Matter: Death

The Death card is in the centre of the spread and must therefore be a primary focus for concentration. Death signifies the loss of Lucy's old way of life: her husband, her security, and even her relationship with friends and acquaintances, for when a marriage dissolves the 'ripple effect' is far-reaching. Death demands that his payment be paid, and the price is mourning. Lucy is using the divorce settlement to vent many of her hurt feelings. In some ways, it is easier to get angry with lawyers and court hearings than it is to face up to personal pain and humiliation. Lucy wants to avoid some of her misery by pursuing a career and a new life, but there is still a lot of mourning to be borne. With the

Eight of Pentacles in the same position in the Minor Arcana layout, her prospects look good for setting up a business and starting afresh. On an emotional level, however, she must first get down to the business of seriously confronting her considerable losses. She will then be able to move forward into the next phase of her life with greater ease, like the souls who paid their coin and secured a new home in the underworld. Those souls who did not have their payment ready were refused entry, and were obliged to wander aimlessly for ever.

POSITION FIVE
Unconscious Hopes and Fears: the Fool

The Fool appears in the sphere of the unconscious, indicating that the time is coming when Lucy will be able to leave her past behind and make the leap into a new and different world. At the moment, she is not ready to make the leap but the possibility is imminent. Lucy is still struggling with the conflicting thoughts and feelings evoked by her recent losses. She does not yet feel confident enough to make the kind of leap of faith the Fool requires. Nevertheless she knows that the time will come soon. She awaits it with both dread and longing.

POSITION SIX
Conscious Desires: the Star

The Star in the sphere of conscious desires is a symbol of hope and optimism which nothing can totally destroy. Despite all Lucy's unhappiness, the Star of Hope appears to give her comfort and direction: the belief that ultimately things will get better. Lucy said she felt a little like Pandora having opened the 'box' of her marriage, which she did not realise contained so many disagreeable aspects. But the fact that Hope alone did not fly away was a cheering thought.

POSITION SEVEN
Top of the Matter: the Emperor

The solid image of the Emperor at the Top of the Matter gave a sense of security and solidity to the reading. It suggested that Lucy would eventually be able to make her ideas concrete, and that she would manage to take over the financial matters involving her family. The Emperor card is a symbol for founding a home, business or tradition on a firm footing. Coming at the top of the reading, it offered a promise that these wishes were possible. Lucy would tap her own sense of ambition and drive to achieve success and stability for herself and her children.

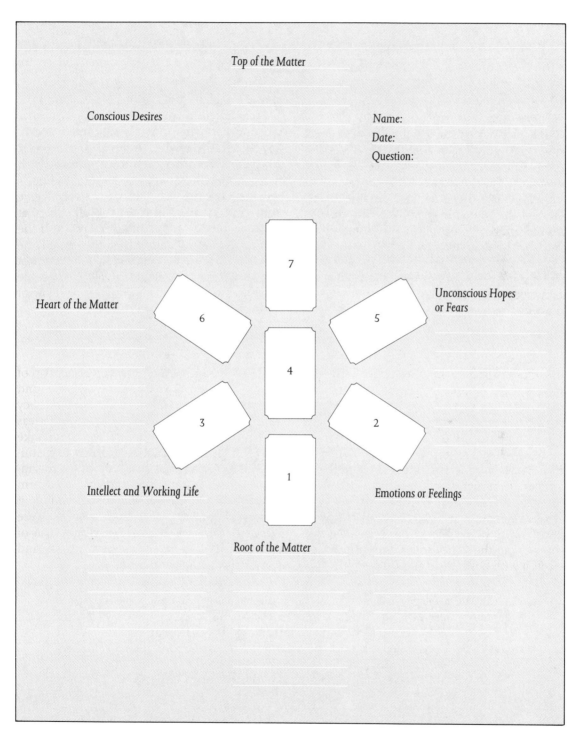

Top of the Matter

Conscious Desires

Name:
Date:
Question:

7

Heart of the Matter

6

Unconscious Hopes
or Fears

5

4

3

2

1

Intellect and Working Life

Emotions or Feelings

Root of the Matter

CONCLUSION

By now, the images on each of the seventy-eight Tarot cards should seem like old friends, comfortable and familiar. If you have performed the exercises set out in this Workbook with effort and care, you will find yourself increasingly in touch with latent intuition. The more times you repeat the exercises, the easier they will become and the more insight you will gain, enabling you to give perceptive readings. Tarot can be a valuable psychological tool which, used sensitively, can help you discover a great deal about yourself, as well as be of help to others.

Each Tarot card is like a magic mirror which reflects an aspect of your inner world. For those of you who immerse yourselves in what the Tarot image has to communicate, it will become like a deep, quiet pool. At first, it seems to reflect only your own image but as you look into it again and again you can discover the inner turmoil of your soul. As you learn ways to gain peace within yourself and with the world, you will reap the reward of your struggles through your study of Tarot.

ACKNOWLEDGEMENTS

Eddison/Sadd Editions acknowledge contributions from the following people:

Editorial Director   Ian Jackson
Creative Director   Nick Eddison
Editor Christine Moffat
Designer   Amanda Barlow
Production   Bob Towell